If intimacy with God is the desi[r...] a lovely tool to encourage and facilitate as you come into his presence.

> —John and Linda Willet
> NC Area Director with Search Ministries, former Grace
> Brethren and Westover Church Pastor, Lecturer with Family
> Life Marriage Conferences (Campus Crusade for Christ)

For those yearning to know God, *Grace for the Journey* provides a simple, systematic formula to record daily reactions and insights to scripture. Sarah's book will be an enormous help in providing "how to's" as well as incentives to move forward in an ongoing adventure of faith.

> —Phyllis Stern
> Regional Speaker Trainer, Stonecroft Ministries, Cary, NC

God told Isaiah that his Word will not return to him without accomplishment. Let it do that through prayer and journaling guided by *Grace for the Journey*. (Isa. 55:11)

> —Dr. Richard H. & Shirilee Little
> Retired Presbyterian Pastor, Author and Lecturer,
> Seventeenth Moderator of the Evangelical Presbyterian Church

GRACE
FOR THE
JOURNEY

GRACE
FOR THE
JOURNEY

Come Boldly

to the

Throne

of

Grace

A DAILY PRAYER GUIDE AND JOURNAL

SARAH BUSH

WinePress Publishing (PO Box 428, Enumclaw, WA 98022) functions only as book publisher. As such, the ultimate design, content, editorial accuracy, and views expressed or implied in this work are those of the author.

Interior Illustrations by Sandra Snarski.

ISBN 13: 978-1-57921-967-3
ISBN 10: 1-57921-967-5
Library of Congress Catalog Card Number: 2008927380

I would like to dedicate this journal to my children who have sacrificed a great deal of time and attention, encouraged me along the way, and kept me accountable by asking their innocent questions. They are the most important reason I write . . . to leave them a legacy of God's love.

CONTENTS

ACKNOWLEDGMENTS

My first expression of thanksgiving goes to my Lord and Savior, Jesus Christ. For if it was not for his saving grace, I never would have come to the understanding of the truth and the eternal treasures of prayer.

I am thankful to my loving husband, Eric, who believed in me and remained confident every step of the way to accomplish this calling on my life to write. He has truly been a pillar of support.

I am thankful to my parents who have left a legacy of loving God and living for Him; who have always prayed for me, been an example to me, and encouraged me.

To all the members of my family, I appreciate your love, words of support, and prayers.

To my MITI friends, my River Oaks Community Church family, my small group, my prayer team, WinePress, and to so many other friends that are too numerous to mention; thank you. You each have been faithful sojourners by my side. You have taken time to pray with and for me approaching the throne on my behalf and on the behalf of my readers. You have faithfully encouraged me, given me insight and ideas, and kept me persevering. God bless you all!

INTRODUCTION

I n our fast-paced society with the tyranny of the urgent beckoning us, spending time alone with God is easily neglected. Often I meet Christians who struggle to prioritize their time, and many desire a resourceful prayer guide and journal to enhance and simplify their daily prayer lives. Realizing the value of prayer and journaling in my life, I saw the need to share what I have created with others.

This journal is a suggested companion book to *The Invitation—Come Boldly to the Throne of Grace*. *The Invitation* is written to explain the benefits of prayer and journaling. It consists of principles from scripture revealing God's intentional desire to dwell with us for his pleasure, purpose, and companionship. Exploring God's intentional pursuit of the forefathers of faith, glancing at the covenant promises, and walking through an overview of the Tabernacle, God's initiative in developing a relationship and life of prayer within us is evident.

The Invitation offers assurance found in Jesus' self-sacrificing love demonstrated in his death and resurrection. He lives to intercede for us; reconciling man to God. Following his example, we should live to pray with confidence approaching the throne of grace.

God persistently extends a continual, permanent invitation welcoming us into his holy presence. God desires a response in the human heart by faith through prayer, studying his Word, and aided journaling. These disciplines cultivate a surrendered heart intended for God's purpose. By bringing hope to individuals in developing a vibrant relationship with God and discovering their unique purpose, God's kingdom is being built and his glory revealed.

Grace for the Journey is a companion journal for practical application containing daily prayer and journal pages. The daily prayer pages are for individual prayers consisting of prearranged scripture verses and available space for listing personal needs, immediate family concerns, and vocational requests. Along with the daily prayer page, each day provides a journal entry page with available space to write personal thoughts and life lessons. Weekly prayer pages are designed with a specific prayer guide listing a variety of topics and scripture verses each day of the week.

Just like running, if I make it a priority first thing in the morning, I usually do it. You will be blessed if you set aside time to put God first in your day. The key to the prayer plan is to develop more dialogue with God, growing in grace to give him glory. Find one or two things you can add to your prayer life and journaling to help develop your spiritual growth. Too often we find ourselves discouraged because we think we ought to be somewhere spiritually we are not. Find a pace that works for you and follow it. This journal is a tool to find grace and not meant to be an absolute.

As a teenager, I made a commitment to the LORD, yet struggled with how to pray. I asked God to give me the desire to pray, to get up early and spend time with him. He has certainly answered by giving me a passion for prayer.

For over twenty-five years I have had a habit of journaling and recording what God teaches me and how he reveals his work in my life. Over the years, I have used various journals and prayer guides, but never was able to locate the two that worked in harmony. This desire led me to create an inspirational book on the benefits of prayer and journaling, sharing personal experiences, along with a useful companion prayer guide and journal for daily use.

My dream is that God would use these materials as a ministry—to restore the human heart in order to find intimacy with the Designer and Creator of our soul. By using this journal, I hope it will help you to become more conscious of God's presence and to remember his faithfulness as you record your prayers and life journey.

My hope is that this book provides a sanctuary for you to grow in a greater understanding of God's unfailing love and in your devotion to prayer. We are designed for a life of prayer and have been given God's Word and His Holy Spirit to equip us with everything we need for prayer. For people who are tentative in the ability to pray or journal, and lack understanding concerning the eternal rewards of both, this journal will be a source of confidence in building your faith. It will equip people who believe in the power of prayer and journaling, but lack the accountability to create consistency and discipline. Individuals who seek achievement may discover a balance of goals and grace.

If you are a new believer, new to prayer, or new to journaling, keep it simple. I recommend you read *The Invitation—Come Boldly to the Throne of Grace* while using the prayer guide and journal. Begin your journey by simply praying through the Daily Prayer page first. Write your thoughts on the journal page as you reflect on God's work in your life. When you have gained confidence, add to your devotional time in the Weekday Prayer page.

My prayer for each one who opens this journal is that you believe in the Jesus Christ as your Savior and Lord and are set free to worship Jesus with a deeper passion for prayer established in love. May you "know this love that surpasses knowledge—that you may be filled to the measure of all the fullness of God" (Eph 3:19). May the love of Christ compel you to pray, "that we who live, no longer live for ourselves but for him who died for us and was raised again" (2 Cor 5:15b).

As the Israelites gathered their manna, enough for each day in the morning, each one gathered as much as they needed. May God give you your daily bread to sustain you, perfectly measured for your need. His supply is enough for each day as you boldly approach the throne receiving grace for your journey.

Through prayer, may you touch the world around you. In the end, at the final trumpet sound, in heaven may you witness your golden bowl of incense overflow as a glory of grace around Jesus' feet, his robe, and rise as a sweet aroma unto him. May you hear the words, "Well done, good and faithful servant! You have been faithful with a few things; I will put you in charge of many things. Come and share your master's happiness!" (Mt 25:23). Let us faithfully approach the throne of grace with confidence in his unfailing love.

R. S. V. P. YOUR FIRST RESPONSE TO THE INVITATION

B efore reading this book you may have questions about your assurance of being saved and possessing eternal life. Your prayer of salvation is the most critical prayer of all. It is the most important decision you will ever make. This prayer is the vital response to the invitation from God to "Come." First, admit that you are sinful and separated from God. *For all have sinned and fall short of the glory of God* (Rom 3:23). Believe Christ died for your sins. *But God demonstrates his own love for us in this: While we were still sinners, Christ died for us* (Rom 5:8). Then commit your life and future to Jesus Christ and accept his free gift of salvation. *For the wages of sin is death, but the gift of God is eternal life in Christ Jesus our Lord* (Rom 6:23). Invite Jesus now to be your Savior, Redeemer, and Friend. Pray and confess a simple prayer like this: *LORD, I confess I am a sinner. I believe Jesus died for all my sins on the cross. I receive his forgiveness and I am now clean. I believe he died, was raised from the dead, and is coming back again. I now commit my life to you. Come, Lord Jesus and dwell within my heart. Fill me with your Holy Spirit. In Jesus Name, Amen.*

If you have prayed this prayer for the first time, know that the angels rejoice in heaven over you! Commit to pray and read God's word daily. Seek fellowship at a Bible teaching church and tell someone who can help you grow spiritually that you made this decision. Jesus said, *Whoever acknowledges me before men, I will also acknowledge him before my Father in heaven. But whoever disowns me before men, I will disown him before my Father in heaven* (Mt 10:32–33).

ARE YOU READY TO PRAY AND JOURNAL?

Since the Garden of Eden, God's desire is to commune with us. After our fellowship was broken by sin, God revealed his presence for hundreds of years sharing his glory in the earthly tabernacle, which was designed and built to meet with him. Now under the new covenant as we respond in prayer by faith and accept Jesus, he abides in our hearts. What an awesome privilege is granted to come into his presence. Be intentional as you approach the throne with reverence.

In your mind, picture entering into the earthly tabernacle. Remember in the new covenant Jesus is the culmination of all that the sanctuary represents. Enter his gates with thanksgiving and his courts with praise, walk by the bronze altar, and accept the sacrifice of the Lamb. Wash off your sins in the bronze basin as you confess and accept his cleansing power and forgiveness. Bring your prayers to the altar of incense releasing the concerns of your heart as a continuous aroma. Enter the Holy of Holies beyond the torn veil and bow humbly in his holy presence, the place of pure intimacy.

INTRODUCTION

As you come into God's presence ask him these questions and listen for his gentle reply:

LORD, show me sins I need to confess?

Are all my relationships healthy and right?

Am I surrendering to your will in all areas of my life?

Am I seeking to glorify and please you above all others?

Am I depending on the Holy Spirit's guidance?

LORD, do I trust you despite what seems to be?

LORD, am I praising you no matter what?

How to Use the
Prayer Journal

This prayer guide and journal is designed to increase prayer and journaling in your quiet time with God. Each day you will begin by being reminded to Enter His Courts with Praise, Enter His Gates with Thanksgiving, Wash with the Cleansing Water—Search and Confess, Linger and Listen, and Apply the Armor of God. These categories are listed at the top of each Daily Prayer page as Praise and Proclaim, Offer Thanks, Search and Confess, Listen and Apply Armor. Suggested scripture references are provided for each category listed above to assist you. Choose only one or two verses from each section to pray until you have worked through all five sections.

After applying the armor of God use your Daily Prayer page and continue in your time of intercession. During the daily prayer time, verses are provided to assist you in praying for yourself, your immediate family, and your activities. Midway through the book you will have an opportunity to insert your own scripture to pray for these topics along with special concerns and a missionary each day.

Use the journal page to record your thoughts or a verse that was meaningful to you from the prayer time or your Bible study. For a more in-depth understanding of journaling, you might find it helpful to read the companion book, *The Invitation—Come Boldly to the Throne of Grace*.

The Sunday through Saturday Weekday Prayer pages provide specific scriptures to pray for a variety of topics. Many of the scriptures I have written as prayers. You may also list your own requests in the space provided. This book can be used once a day or like bookends . . . Daily Prayers/Journal in the morning and Weekday Prayers at night.

Here's how to get started: (Suggested readings are given for each section found in *The Invitation*, but are not required as part of your prayer time.)

1. **Enter His Courts with Praise—Praise and Proclaim—** Each day choose a praise verse from the pages "Enter His Courts with Praise." Use these to enter into God's presence. Use the verses listed to tell God he is wonderful. Praise him for his attributes: his holiness, majesty, power, splendor, goodness, kindness, patience, compassion, mercy, grace, love, forgiveness, and so much more! When we recall who God is, our perspective on life issues and circumstances change. Explore the Hebrew Names of God to aid in your worship. Suggested reading in *The Invitation*: Enter His Courts with Praise and His Gates with Thanksgiving.

2. **Enter His Gates with Thanksgiving—Offer Thanks—** Each day spend time reading a verse from the list "Enter His Gates with Thanksgiving." Give thanks to God for who he is and the many blessings in your life. God commands us to give thanks. A heart of gratitude can change your attitude. Thank God for your physical, spiritual, and monetary blessings. For more ideas refer to the chapter—Enter His Courts with Praise and His Gates with Thanksgiving in *The Invitation*.

3. **Wash with the Cleansing Water—Search and Confess—** Each day choose a verse from the section "Wash with the Cleansing Water—Search and Confess" pages and examine your heart and mind for any thought that is not the mind of Christ. Ask him to search your heart and see if there is any offensive way in you. Confess the wrongdoing the Spirit brings to mind. Learn more about confession in the companion book in the chapter titled Cleanse with the Living Water—Search and Confess.

4. **Linger and Listen—**After you examine your heart see what verse speaks to you from the pages titled "Linger and Listen." Pray over the verse and be still, keeping your mind clear. If an abstract thought comes in to interrupt, take a moment, write it down, and go back to worship and your prayers. To enhance this time it may be helpful to read the chapter—Meet with God Beyond the Veil in *The Invitation*.

5. **Apply the Armor of God—**Each day as you engage in the spiritual battle, remember to put on your coat of armor as you glance over the pages and meditate on verses from "Daily Apply Your Armor." For more insight refer to the chapter—Engaged in the Spiritual Battle, located in the book.

Offer prayers for yourself and others:

Daily—Scriptures and space are provided to pray for personal needs, immediate family, your activities for the day, special concerns (people, or situations you are burdened to pray for every day) and a missionary. As you are led to scriptures to pray for others, record those as your prayer.

- Pray for a greater love and commitment to God and to your family; spiritual growth, wisdom, understanding of God's Word, knowledge and belief in your identity in Christ, God's will, healthy relationships, personal

discipline, health, strength, faithfulness and stewardship of time, talents and money, assistance in ministry,
and evangelism.

- Sometimes God will prompt you to be the answer to a
prayer by taking action in some way. Write it down, circle
it and follow through in obedience. List any scripture
promise by your requests. Faithfully record how God
answers your prayers in the left margin. Keep your list
brief. Write down specific impressions the Holy Spirit
leads you to pray. For more prayers refer to the complete
list of prayer references within the Bible and topics A–Z
located in the back of *The Invitation—Come Boldly to the
Throne of Grace.*

Journal Comments: Is God's personal message important
enough for you to write it down to be remembered? God says,
"Keep my commands and you will live; guard my teachings as
the apple of your eye. Bind them on your fingers; write them
on the tablet of your heart (Prv 7:2–3). By journaling, God's
Word is effectively written on the tablet of your heart. Writing
helps us to clarify our purpose and remember his work in our
lives. "The LORD confides in those who fear him; he makes his
covenant known to them" (Ps 25:14). Your journal entries are
building blocks to strengthen your faith as you journey with
God leaving a legacy for those who follow.

Weekday Categories—On each day of the week you will
discover a prayer guide offering different topics.

Sunday

- **Your Church**—individual concerns, heart condition of
the church, spiritual growth, service
- **Leadership**—pastors, staff and their families, elders and
their families, teachers
- **Ministries of the Church**—salvation of seekers, specific
needs of the church, Bible studies, outreach

- **Lost and Unrepentant**—unsaved, those with hardened hearts

Monday

- **Missionaries**—those you help and serve on the local and overseas mission fields
- **Ministry**—your God-given ministry, serving within the church or building of the body of Christ
- **Poor and Hungry**—within your community, in America, and around the world

Tuesday

- **Thanking God for His Promises**—all God's promises are "Yes" in Christ Jesus! Thank God for the promises he's given you
- **Teens and Youth**—for strength in the current pressures and future of next generation
- **Trials/Troubles of Your Heart**—peace and trust in the circumstances
- **Authorities/Leaders**—government, President, congressional representatives, military, state officials, county and city officials, courts, law enforcement, local schools (Locate officials at www.us.gov.)

Wednesday

- **Waiting on the LORD**—be still before the LORD
- **Worship**—sing praises to the LORD
- **Wounded and Sick**—the hurting who need healing
- **Peace in Jerusalem**—God commands that we pray for peace in Jerusalem

Thursday

- **Thanksgiving**—material, physical, spiritual, eternal blessings

- **Extended Family**—parents, siblings, aunts, uncles, cousins, grandparents, grandchildren, and their spouses
- **Enemies, Persecutors and EGR's** * (Rick Warren's phrase for those whom Extra Grace is Required)

Friday

- **Friends and Neighbors**—local, long-distance
- **Coworkers**—outreach opportunities, relationships, morale
- **Concerns and Ministries in your Community, in America, and Around the World**—current events, your sphere of influence, activities

Saturday

- **Special Heartfelt Burdens**—concerns for others that are heavy on your heart
- **Prayer for the Church and Pastors Locally, in America, and Around the World**—protection and revival
- **Prepare Your Heart for Worship**—spend time asking God to prepare your heart for worship

SETTING FURTHER GOALS

Once a week: After you have completed a week of the prayer journal, begin a regular routine of reviewing your journal and looking over your prayer requests. Check or mark answers to your prayers. Write PRAISE when a prayer is answered. Pause and make sure you give him thanks for all he is doing and has done in response to your prayers. Meditate on and hold close the teachings that God has given you. Review your heart concerns. Add additional notes.

Once a Month: Take an hour or two and read through your journal and prayer requests so you can begin to take hold and remember all that God is "up to" in your life. As you remember, God may bring people into your life with whom you need to share a scripture or something he placed on your heart. Mark this goal on your calendar so you will follow through.

Once a Year: Read *The Invitation*, again, and pick out one or two ideas you can apply to your prayer life and journaling. Pick a date after a year of journal use for you take time to read through your journals and prayer requests. This is a time to remember God's work in your life and rejoice for his presence and revelation to you.

PERSONAL PRAYER

Enter His Courts with Praise

Enter his gates with thanksgiving and his courts with praise; give thanks to him and praise his name (Ps 100:4).

He is your praise; he is your God, who performed for you those great and awesome wonders you saw with your own eyes (Dt 10:21).

I will proclaim the name of the LORD. Oh, praise the greatness of our God! (Dt 32:3).

Praise be to the LORD, who this day has not left you without a kinsman-redeemer. May he become famous throughout Israel! (Ru 4:14).

The LORD lives! Praise be to my Rock! Exalted be God, the Rock, my Savior! (2 Sm 22:47).

Praise be to the LORD, who has given rest to his people Israel just as he promised. Not one word has failed of all the good promises he gave through his servant Moses (1 Kgs 8:56).

Save us, O God our Savior; . . . that we may glory in your praise (1 Chr 16:35).

Praise be to the LORD, the God of Israel, from everlasting to everlasting. Then all the people said "Amen" and "Praise the LORD" (1 Chr 16:36).

Then he said: "Praise be to the LORD, the God of Israel, who with his hands has fulfilled what he promised with his mouth . . ." (2 Chr 6:4).

Sing to the LORD and praise him for the splendor of his holiness (2 Chr 20:21b).

Naked I came from my mother's womb, and naked I will depart. The LORD gave and the LORD has taken away; may the name of the LORD be praised (Jb 1:21).

I will praise you, O LORD, with all my heart (Ps 9:1a).

The poor will eat and be satisfied; they who seek the LORD will praise him—may your hearts live forever! (Ps 22:26).

Enter His Courts with Praise

PRAISE

Yet you are enthroned as the Holy One; you are the praise of Israel (Ps 22:3).

Praise be to the LORD, for he showed his wonderful love to me (Ps 31:21a).

Sing joyfully to the LORD, you righteous; it is fitting for the upright to praise him (Ps 33:1).

I will praise you, O LORD my God, with all my heart; I will glorify your name forever. For great is your love toward me (Ps 86:12–13a).

I will extol the LORD at all times; his praise will always be on my lips (Ps 34:1).

My tongue will speak of your righteousness and of your praises all day long (Ps 35:28).

He put a new song in my mouth, a hymn of praise to our God (Ps 40:3a).

Like your name, O God, your praise reaches to the ends of the earth; your right hand is filled with righteousness (Ps 48:10).

In God, whose word I praise, in God I trust; I will not be afraid. What can mortal man do to me? (Ps 56:4).

Praise be to God, who has not rejected my prayer or withheld his love from me! (Ps 66:20).

Praise be to the LORD, to God our Savior, who daily bears our burdens (Ps 68:19).

But as for me, I will always have hope; I will praise you more and more (Ps 71:14).

Let them praise your great and awesome name—he is holy (Ps 99:3).

Praise the LORD, O my soul. O LORD, my God, you are very great; you are clothed with splendor and majesty (Ps 104:1).

Then they believed his promises and sang his praise (Ps 106:12).

PRAISE

Enter His Courts with Praise

From the rising of the sun to the place where it sets, the name of the LORD *is to be praised* (Ps 113:3).

I praise you because I am fearfully and wonderfully made; your works are wonderful, I know that full well (Ps 139:14).

Great is the LORD *and most worthy of praise; his greatness no one can fathom. All you have made will praise you, O* LORD; *your saints will extol you* (Ps 145:3–4).

The LORD *reigns forever, your God, O Zion, for all generations. Praise the* LORD (Ps 146:10).

O LORD, *you are my God; I will exalt you and praise your name, for in perfect faithfulness you have done marvelous things, things planned long ago* (Is 25:1).

The living, the living—they praise you, as I am doing today; fathers tell their children about your faithfulness (Is 38:19).

My mouth is filled with your praise, declaring your splendor all day long (Ps 71:8).

Praise the LORD, *O my soul; all my inmost being, praise his holy name. Praise the* LORD, *O my soul, and forget not all his benefits – who forgives all your sins and heals all your diseases, who redeems your life from the pit and crowns you with love and compassion, who satisfies your desires with good things . . . for as high as the heavens are above the earth, so great is his love for those who fear him . . . Praise the* LORD, *all his works everywhere in his dominion. Praise the* LORD, *O my soul* (Ps 103:1–5, 11, 22).

I will praise you with an upright heart as I learn your righteous laws (Ps 119:7).

At that time Jesus said, "I praise you, Father, Lord of heaven and earth, because you have hidden these things from the wise and learned, and revealed them to little children" (Mt 11:25).

Enter His Courts with Praise

Praise be to the LORD, the God of Israel, because he has come and has redeemed his people (Lk 1:68).

Was no one found to return and give praise to God except this foreigner? (Lk 17:18).

Theirs are the patriarchs, and from them is traced the human ancestry of Christ, who is God over all, forever praised! Amen (Rom 9:5).

Praise be to the God and Father of our Lord Jesus Christ, who has blessed us in the heavenly realms with every spiritual blessing in Christ (Eph 1:3).

To the praise of his glorious grace, which he has freely given us in the One he loves (Eph 1:6).

In order that we who were the first to hope in Christ, might be for the praise of his glory (Eph 1:12).

His glory covered the heavens and his praise filled the earth (Hab 3:3b).

Praise be to the God and Father of our Lord Jesus Christ! In his great mercy he has given us new birth into a living hope through the resurrection of Jesus Christ from the dead (1 Pt 1:3).

However, if you suffer as a Christian, do not be ashamed, but praise God that you bear that name (1 Pt 4:16).

In a loud voice they sang: "Worthy is the Lamb, who was slain, to receive power and wealth and wisdom and strength and honor and glory and praise!" (Rv 5:12).

Hebrew Names of God

JEHOVAH
The Self-Existent One Who Reveals Himself
Revelation 1:8, Romans 1:17–20, Psalm 103

JEHOVAH ROPHE
The LORD Heals
Exodus 15:22–27, 2 Chronicles 7:14, Psalm 147:3, Isaiah19:22
Isaiah 53:5, Matthew 8:16, 17, Luke 4:18, 1 Peter 2:24, 25

JEHOVAH ROHI
The LORD Our Shepherd
Psalm 100:3, Psalm 23, Isaiah 53:6, Jeremiah 23:16
John 10:1–17, John 10:26–33, John 21:17

JEHOVAH-M'KADDESH
The LORD Who Sanctifies
Exodus 1:13, Exodus 19:2–6, John 17:15, 19
1 Thessalonians 4:3–8, 5:23, Hebrews 10:10–14, 1 Peter 2:9

JEHOVAH-SHALOM
The LORD Our Peace
Numbers 6:22–27, Isaiah 9:6, Jeremiah 29:11, John 14:27
Romans 5:1, Philippians 4:4–9

JEHOVAH-SHAMMAH
LORD is Present
Deuteronomy 12:7, 2 Chronicles 6:19, Psalm 16:11
Psalm 1:6, Psalm 31:30, Psalm 89:15
Proverbs 18:16, Ezekiel 48:35, John 16:7
Hebrews 13:5, Revelation 21:3

Hebrew Names of God

JEHOVAH-JIREH
The LORD Our Provider
Genesis 22:1–19, Job 3:16, Matthew 6:7, 8, Acts 8:32
Romans 8:32, Philippians 4:19

JEHOVAH-TSIDKENU
The LORD Our Righteousness
Matthew 5:6, John 1:12, John 1:29, Romans 3:22
Romans 6:18, 2 Corinthians 5:21

JEHOVAH-NISSI
The LORD Our Banner and Victory
Exodus 14:13, Deuteronomy 20:3–4, Romans 8:17
2 Corinthians 2:14, Ephesians 3:20–21
Ephesians 6:10, 2 Timothy 4:7

EL SHADDAI
The LORD Our Sufficiency and Caregiver
Exodus 15:2, 13, 2 Samuel 22:33, 1 Chronicles 16:27
Psalm 18:32, 2 Corinthians 12:9, 1 Peter 5:7

EL ELYON
The Most High God
Numbers 24:16, Deuteronomy 32:8, 2 Samuel 22:14
Psalm 7:8, 10, Psalm 1:1, 9, Psalm 9:2
Psalm 21:7, Psalm 47:2, Psalm 57:2
Psalm 78:35, Psalm 83:13, Daniel 4:2

Enter His Gates with Thanksgiving

Enter his gates with thanksgiving and his courts with praise; give thanks to him and praise his name (Ps 100:4).

I will give thanks to the LORD because of his righteousness and will sing praise to the name of the LORD Most High (Ps 7:17).

That my heart may sing to you and not be silent, O LORD my God, I will give you thanks forever (Ps 30:12).

I will praise God's name in song and glorify him with thanksgiving (Ps 69:30).

We give thanks to you, O God, we give thanks, for your Name is near; men tell of your wonderful deeds (Ps 75:1).

Give thanks to the LORD, call on his name; make known among the nations what he has done (Ps 105:1).

Let them give thanks to the LORD for his unfailing love and his wonderful deeds for men (Ps 107:8).

Give thanks to the LORD, for he is good; his love endures forever (Ps 118:1).

The LORD's right hand is lifted high; the LORD's right hand has done mighty things! I will not die but live, and will proclaim what the LORD has done. The LORD has chastened me severely, but he has not given me over to death. Open for me the gates of righteousness; I will enter and give thanks to the LORD. This is the gate of the LORD through which the righteous may enter (Ps 118:16–20).

I will give you thanks, for you answered me; you have become my salvation (Ps 118:21).

The LORD will surely comfort Zion and will look with compassion on all her ruins; he will make her deserts like Eden, her wastelands like the garden of the LORD. Joy and gladness will be found in her, thanksgiving and the sound of singing (Is 51:3).

Enter His Gates with Thanksgiving

And he took bread, gave thanks and broke it, and gave it to them, saying, "This is my body given for you; do this in remembrance of me" (Lk 22:19).

Thanks be to God—through Jesus Christ our Lord! (Rom 7:25a).

I always thank God for you because of his grace given you in Christ Jesus (1 Cor 1:4).

Cry out, save us, O God our Savior; gather us and deliver us from the nations, that we may give thanks to your holy name, that we may glory in your praise (1 Chr 16:35).

When all the Israelites saw the fire coming down and the glory of the Lord above the temple, they knelt on the pavement with their faces to the ground, and they worshiped and gave thanks to the LORD, saying, "He is good; his love endures forever" (2 Chr 7:3).

With praise and thanksgiving they sang to the LORD: "He is good; his love to Israel endures forever . . ." (Ezr 3:11).

I am still confident of this: I will see the goodness of the LORD in the land of the living (Ps 27:13).

He threw himself at Jesus' feet and thanked him—and he was a Samaritan (Lk 17:16).

You will be made rich in every way so that you can be generous on every occasion, and through us your generosity will result in thanksgiving to God (2 Cor 9:11).

But thanks be to God, who always leads us in triumphal procession in Christ and through us spreads everywhere the fragrance of the knowledge of him (2 Cor 2:14).

All this is for your benefit, so that the grace that is reaching more and more people may cause thanksgiving to overflow to the glory of God (2 Cor 4:15).

THANKS

Enter His Gates with Thanksgiving

Thanks be to God for his indescribable gift! (2 Cor 9:15).

For this reason, ever since I heard about your faith in the Lord Jesus and your love for all the saints, I have not stopped giving thanks for you, remembering you in my prayers (Eph 1:15–16).

Always giving thanks to God the Father for everything, in the name of our Lord Jesus Christ (Eph 5:20).

I thank my God every time I remember you in my prayers (Phil 1:4).

We always thank God, the Father of our Lord Jesus Christ, when we pray for you, because we have heard of your faith in Christ Jesus and of the love you have for all the saints— (Col 1:3–4).

We ought always to thank God for you, brothers, and rightly so, because your faith is growing more and more, and the love every one of you has for each other is increasing (2 Thes 1:3).

For everything God created is good, and nothing is to be rejected if it is received with thanksgiving (1 Tm 4:4).

Wash with the Cleansing Water—Search and Confess

Acknowledge the God of your father, and serve him with wholehearted devotion and with a willing mind, for the LORD searches every heart and understands every motive behind the thoughts. If you seek him, he will be found by you: but if you forsake him, he will reject you forever (1 Chr 28:9).

You must search out my faults and probe after my sin (Jb 10:6).

When you are on your beds, search your hearts and be silent (Ps 4:4b).

O righteous God, who searches minds and hearts, bring to an end the violence of the wicked and make the righteous secure (Ps 7:9).

Then I acknowledged my sin to you and did not cover up my iniquity. I said, "I will confess my transgressions to the LORD"—and you forgave the guilt of my sin (Ps 32:5).

O LORD, you have searched me and you know me (Ps 139:1).

Search me, O God, and know my heart; test me and know my anxious thoughts. See if there is any offensive way in me, and lead me in the way everlasting (Ps 139:23–24).

The lamp of the LORD searches the spirit of a man; it searches out his inmost being (Prv 20:27).

There is a time for everything . . . a time to search . . . a time to be silent (Eccl 3:1, 6a, 7b).

Surely the arm of the LORD is not too short to save, nor his ear too dull to hear. But your iniquities have separated you from your God; your sins have hidden his face from you, so that he will not hear (Is 59:1–2).

I the LORD search the heart and examine the mind, to reward a man according to his conduct, according to what his deeds deserve (Jer 17:10).

At that time I will search Jerusalem with lamps and punish those who are complacent, who are like wine left on its dregs, who think, "The LORD will do nothing, either good or bad" (Zep 1:12).

Wash with the Cleansing Water—Search and Confess

And he who searches our hearts knows the mind of the Spirit, because the Spirit intercedes for the saints in accordance with God's will (Rom 8:27).

For it is with your heart that you believe and are justified, and it is with your mouth that you confess and are saved (Rom 10:10).

But God has revealed it to us by his Spirit. The Spirit searches all things, even the deep things of God (1 Cor 2:10).

Now make confession to the LORD, the God of your fathers, and do his will. Separate yourselves from the peoples around you and from your foreign wives (Ezr 10:11).

Let your ear be attentive and your eyes open to hear the prayer your servant is praying before you day and night for your servants, the people of Israel. I confess the sins we Israelites, including myself and my father's house, have committed against you (Neh 1:6).

"Who can discern his errors? Forgive my hidden faults. Keep your servant also from willful sins; may they not rule over me. Then will I be blameless, innocent of great transgression. May the words of my mouth and the meditation of my heart be pleasing in your sight, O LORD, my Rock and my Redeemer" (Ps 19:12–14).

I confess my iniquity; I am troubled by my sin (Ps 38:18).

Have mercy on me, O God, according to your unfailing love; according to your great compassion blot out my transgressions. Wash away all my iniquity and cleanse me from my sin. For I know my transgressions, and my sin is always before me. Against you, you only, have I sinned and done what is evil in your sight, Hide your face from my sins and blot out all my iniquity. Create in me a pure heart, O God, and renew a steadfast spirit within me. Do not cast me from your presence or take your Holy Spirit from me. Restore to me the joy of your salvation and grant me a willing spirit, to sustain me (Ps 51:1–4, 10–12).

He who conceals his sins does not prosper, but whoever confesses and renounces them finds mercy (Prv 28:13).

Wash with the Cleansing Water—Search and Confess

I prayed to the LORD *my God and confessed: "O* LORD*, the great and awesome God, who keeps his covenant of love with all who love him and obey his commands"* (Dn 9:4).

Many of those who believed now came and openly confessed their evil deeds (Acts 19:18).

The Lord knows those who are his, and, "Everyone who confesses the name of the Lord must turn away from wickedness" (2 Tm 2:19b).

Through Jesus, therefore, let us continually offer to God a sacrifice of praise—the fruit of lips that confess his name (Heb 13:15).

Therefore confess your sins to each other and pray for each other so that you may be healed (Jas 5:16).

If we confess our sins, he is faithful and just and will forgive us our sins and purify us from all unrighteousness (1 Jn 1:9).

Read the confessional sin passages regularly. Examine your heart.

And he said, "What comes out of a man, that defiles a man. For from within, out of the heart of men, proceed evil thoughts, adulteries, fornications, murders, thefts, covetousness, wickedness, deceit, lewdness, an evil eye, blasphemy, pride, foolishness. All these evil things come from within and defile a man" (Mk 7:20–23 NKJV).

Put to death, therefore, whatever belongs to your earthly nature: sexual immorality, impurity, lust, evil desires and greed, which is idolatry. Because of these, the wrath of God is coming. You used to walk in these ways, in the life you once lived. But now you must rid yourselves of all such things as these: anger, rage, malice, slander, and filthy language from your lips. Do not lie to each other, since you have taken off your old self with its practices and have put on the new self, which is being renewed in knowledge in the image of its Creator (Col 3:5–10).

Wash with the Cleansing Water—Search and Confess

The acts of the sinful nature are obvious: sexual immorality, impurity and debauchery; idolatry and witchcraft; hatred, discord, jealousy, fits of rage, selfish ambition, dissensions, factions and envy; drunkenness, orgies, and the like. I warn you, as I did before, that those who live like this will not inherit the kingdom of God (Gal 5:19–21).

But the fruit of the Spirit is love, joy, peace, patience, kindness, goodness, faithfulness, gentleness and self-control. Against such things there is no law. Those who belong to Christ Jesus have crucified the sinful nature with its passions and desires. Since we live by the Spirit, let us keep in step with the Spirit. Let us not become conceited, provoking and envying each other (Gal 5:22–26).

Instead, you yourselves cheat and do wrong, and you do this to your brothers. Do you not know that the wicked will not inherit the kingdom of God? Do not be deceived: Neither the sexually immoral nor idolaters nor adulterers nor male prostitutes nor homosexual offenders nor thieves nor the greedy nor drunkards nor slanderers nor swindlers will inherit the kingdom of God. And that is what some of you were. But you were washed, you were sanctified, you were justified in the name of the Lord Jesus Christ and by the Spirit of our God (1 Cor 6:8–11).

He said to me: "It is done. I am the Alpha and the Omega, the Beginning and the End. To him who is thirsty I will give to drink without cost from the spring of the water of life. He who overcomes will inherit all this, and I will be his God and he will be my son. But the cowardly, the unbelieving, the vile, the murderers, the sexually immoral, those who practice magic arts, the idolaters and all liars—their place will be in the fiery lake of burning sulfur. This is the second death" (Rev 21:6–8).

Linger and Listen

Listen, O heavens, and I will speak; hear, O earth, the words of my mouth (Dt 32:1).

Speak LORD, for your servant is listening (1 Sm 3:9b).

But they would not listen and were as stiff-necked as their fathers, who did not trust in the LORD their God (2 Kgs 17:14).

Joshua said to the Israelites, "Come here and listen to the words of the LORD your God" (Josh 3:9).

Do you listen in on God's council? (Jb 15:8a).

Pay attention, Job, and listen to me; be silent, and I will speak (Jb 33:31).

If my people would but listen to me, if Israel would follow my ways (Ps 81:13).

Be still before the LORD and wait patiently for him; do not fret when men succeed in their ways, when they carry out their wicked schemes (Ps 37:7).

Be still, and know that I am God; I will be exalted among the nations, I will be exalted in the earth (Ps 46:10).

O God, do not keep silent; be not quiet, O God, be not still (Ps 83:1).

I will listen to what God the LORD will say; he promises peace to his people, his saints—but let them not return to folly (Ps 85:8).

But I have stilled and quieted my soul (Ps 131:2a).

Let the wise listen and add to their learning, and let the discerning get guidance (Prv 1:5).

But whoever listens to me will live in safety and be at ease, without fear of harm (Prv 1:33).

Linger and Listen

He who answers before listening—that is his folly and his shame (Prv 18:13).

Listen, for I have worthy things to say; I open my lips to speak what is right (Prv 8:6).

Listen to me, O Jacob, Israel, whom I have called: I am he; I am the first and I am the last (Is 48:12).

He wakens me morning by morning, wakens my ear to listen like one being taught (Is 50:4b).

Listen to me, you who pursue righteousness and who seek the LORD (Is 51:1a).

But if you do not listen, I will weep in secret because of your pride; my eyes will weep bitterly, overflowing with tears, because the LORD's flock will be taken captive (Jer 13:17).

Perhaps they will listen and each will turn from his evil way (Jer 26:3a).

"Son of man, listen carefully and take to heart all the words I speak to you" (Ez 3:10).

The great day of the LORD is near—near and coming quickly. Listen! (Zep 1:14).

Jesus called the crowd to him and said, "Listen and understand" (Mt 15:10).

"This is my Son, whom I love; with him I am well pleased. Listen to him!" (Mt 17:5b).

The large crowd listened to him with delight (Mk 12:37b).

Therefore consider carefully how you listen. Whoever has will be given more; whoever does not have, even what he thinks he has will be taken from him (Lk 8:18).

She had a sister called Mary, who sat at the Lord's feet listening to what he said (Lk 10:39).

Linger and Listen

The bride belongs to the bridegroom. The friend who attends the bridegroom waits and listens for him, and is full of joy when he hears the bridegroom's voice (Jn 3:29a).

My sheep listen to my voice; I know them, and they follow me (Jn 10:27).

I have much more to say to you, more than you can now bear. But when he, the Spirit of truth, comes, he will guide you into all truth. He will not speak on his own; he will speak only what he hears, and he will tell you what is yet to come (Jn 16:12–13).

"You are a king, then!" said Pilate. Jesus answered, "You are right in saying I am a king. In fact, for this reason I was born, and for this I came into the world, to testify to the truth. Everyone on the side of truth listens to me" (Jn 18:37).

He who belongs to God hears what God says (Jn 8:47a).

It was good of you to come. Now we are all here in the presence of God to listen (Acts 10:33b).

Everyone should be quick to listen (Jas 1:19b).

This day I call heaven and earth as witnesses against you that I have set before you life and death, blessings, and curses. Now choose life, so that you and your children may live and that you may love the LORD *your God, listen to his voice, and hold fast to him. For the* LORD *is your life* (Dt 30:19–20a).

Apply the Armor of God

Put on the full armor of God, so that when the day of evil comes, you may be able to stand your ground, and after you have done everything to stand. Stand firm then . . . And pray in the Spirit on all occasions with all kinds of prayers and requests. Ephesians 6:13–18

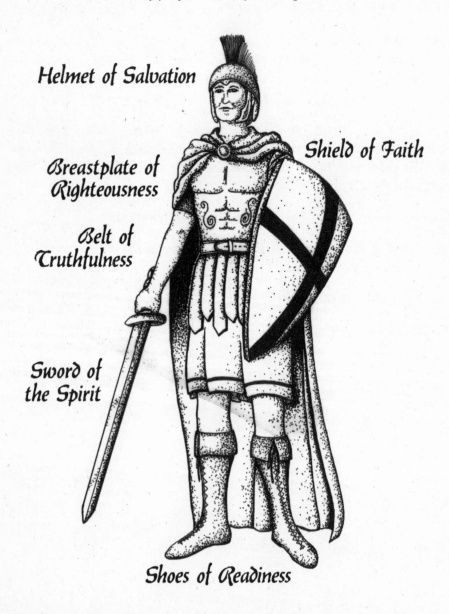

Helmet of Salvation

Breastplate of Righteousness

Belt of Truthfulness

Shield of Faith

Sword of the Spirit

Shoes of Readiness

Daily Apply Your Armor

The night is nearly over; the day is almost here. So let us put aside the deeds of darkness and put on the armor of light. Romans 13:12

1. Belt of Truth Buckled Around Your Waist

He gave him all the plans of all the spirit had put in his mind for the courts of the temple (1 Chr 28:12).

Acknowledge the God of your father and serve him with wholehearted devotion and with a willing mind for the LORD searches every heart and understands every motive behind the thoughts (1 Chr 28:9a).

Dear children, you belong to God. You have not accepted the teachings of the false prophets. That's because the One who is in you is more powerful than the one who is in the world (1 Jn 4:4 NIRV).

May your love and truth always protect me. For troubles without number surround me; my sins have overtaken me, and I cannot see (Ps 40:11b–12a).

Do not conform any longer to the pattern of this world, but be transformed by the renewing of your mind. Then you will be able to test and approve what God's will is—his good, pleasing and perfect will (Rom 12:2).

We are more than conquerors through him who loved us (Rom 8:37).

Your attitude should be the same as that of Christ Jesus (Phil 2:5).

Finally, brothers, whatever is true, whatever is noble, whatever is right, whatever is pure, whatever is lovely, whatever is admirable—if anything is excellent or praiseworthy—think about such things (Phil 4:8).

2. Breastplate of Righteousness in Place

By faith in Christ exists the covering of righteousness for every believer.

If you do what is right, will you not be accepted? But if you do not do what is right, sin is crouching at your door; it desires to have you, but you must master it (Gen 4:7).

Fashion a breastpiece for making decisions—the true work of a skilled craftsman (Ex 28:15a).

The work of righteousness will be peace; the effect of righteousness will be quietness and confidence forever (Is 32:17 KJV / NIV).

It is because of him that you are in Christ Jesus, who has become for us wisdom from God—that is, our righteousness, holiness and redemption (1 Cor 1:30).

As servants of God we commend ourselves in every way: in great endurance; in troubles, hardship and distresses; in beatings, imprisonments and riots; in hard work, sleepless nights and hunger; in purity, understanding, patience and kindness; in the Holy Spirit and in sincere love; in truthful speech and in the power of God; with weapons of righteousness in the right hand and in the left; through glory and dishonor, bad report and good report; . . . known, yet regarded as unknown; dying, and yet we live on; beaten, and yet not killed; sorrowful, yet always rejoicing; poor, yet making many rich; having nothing, and yet possessing everything (2 Cor 6:4–10).

Each one is tempted when, by his own evil desire, he is dragged away and enticed. Then, after desire has conceived, it gives birth to sin; and sin, when it is full-grown, gives birth to death (Jas 1:14–15).

Dear friends, I urge you, as aliens and strangers in the world, to abstain from sinful desires, which war against your soul (1 Pt 2:11).

3. Feet Fitted with Readiness of Gospel of Peace

There is a future for the man of peace (Ps 37:37b).

Great peace have they who love your law, and nothing can make them stumble (Ps 119:165).

(The way of wisdom) Her ways are pleasant ways, and all her paths are peace (Prv 3:17).

Doing what is right will bring peace and rest. When my people do that, they will stay calm and trust in the LORD forever (Is 32:17 NIRV).

My covenant was with him, a covenant of life and peace (Mal 2:5a).

He has come . . . to guide our feet into path of peace (Lk 68, 79b).

Therefore, since we have been justified through faith, we have peace with God through our Lord Jesus Christ (Rom 5:1).

For he himself is our peace, who has made the two one and has destroyed the barrier, the dividing wall of hostility (Eph 2:14).

And the peace of God, which transcends all understanding, will guard your hearts and your minds in Christ Jesus (Phil 4:7).

Be self-controlled and alert. Your enemy the devil prowls around like a roaring lion looking for someone to devour. Resist him, standing firm in the faith, because you know that your brothers throughout the world are undergoing the same kind of sufferings (1 Pt 5:8–9).

4. Take Up the Shield of Faith

Be alert to extinguish all the flaming arrows of the evil one. Our impenetrable Shield, our protection is Jesus Christ our Lord and King.

Let the beloved of the LORD rest secure in him, for he shields him all day long, and the one the LORD loves rests between his shoulders (Dt 33:12).

He is a shield for all who take refuge in him (2 Sm 22:31b).

Prepare your shields, both large and small, and march out for battle! (Jer 46:3).

The LORD is my Strength and my [impenetrable] Shield; my heart trusts in, relies on, and confidently leans on Him, and I am helped; therefore my heart greatly rejoices, and with my song will I praise Him. The LORD is their [unyielding] Strength, and he is the Stronghold of salvation to [me] His anointed (Ps 28:7–8, AMP).

Indeed, our shield belongs to the LORD, our king to the Holy One of Israel. Once you spoke in a vision, to your faithful people you said: "I have bestowed strength on a warrior; I have exalted a young man from among the people" (Ps 89:18–19).

Jesus answered, "It is written: 'Man does not live on bread alone, but on every word that comes from the mouth of God'" (Mt 4:4).

Deliver us from the evil one (Mt 6:13).

The apostles said to the Lord, "Increase our faith!" (Lk 17:5).

But my righteous one will live by faith. And if he shrinks back, I will not be pleased with him. But we are not of those who shrink back and are destroyed, but of those who believe and are saved (Heb 10:38–39).

Submit yourselves, then, to God. Resist the devil, and he will flee from you (Jas 4:7).

Fight the good fight of the faith. Take hold of the eternal life to which you were called when you made your good confession in the presence of many witnesses (1 Tm 6:12).

Our good news didn't come to you only in words. It came with power. It came with the Holy Spirit's help. He gave us complete faith in what we were preaching (1 Thes 1:5 NIRV).

You, dear children, are from God and have overcome them, because the one who is in you is greater than the one who is in the world (1 Jn 4:4).

The LORD is my strength and my shield; my heart trusts in him, and I am helped (Ps 28:7a).

For surely, O LORD, you bless the righteous; you surround them with your favor as with a shield (Ps 5:12).

5. Put on the Helmet of Salvation

Be made new in the attitude of your minds (Eph 4:23).

If you forgive anyone, I also forgive him. And what I have forgiven—if there was anything to forgive—I have forgiven in the sight of Christ for your sake, in order that Satan might not outwit us. For we are not unaware of his schemes (2 Cor 2:10–11).

We demolish arguments and every pretension that sets itself up against the knowledge of God, and we take captive every thought to make it obedient to Christ (2 Cor 10:5).

The quiet words of the wise are more to be heeded than the shouts of a ruler of fools. Wisdom is better than weapons of war . . . (Eccl 9:17–18).

For who has known the mind of the Lord that he may instruct him? But we have the mind of Christ (1 Cor 2:16).

Love the Lord your God with all your heart and with all your soul and with all your mind and with all your strength (Mk 12:30).

Those who live according to the sinful nature have their minds set on what that nature desires; but those who live in accordance with the Spirit have their minds set on what the Spirit desires (Rom 8:5).

I will fear no evil, for you are with me (Ps 23:4b).

But since we belong to the day, let us be self-controlled, putting on faith and love as a breastplate, and the hope of salvation as a helmet (1 Thes 5:8).

For God did not give us a spirit of timidity, but a spirit of power, of love and of self-discipline (a sound mind) (2 Tm 1:7NIV, NKJV).

6. Take Up the Sword of the Spirit—the Word of God and Prayer

The LORD has saved you. He keeps you safe. He helps you. He's like a glorious Sword to you (Dt 33:29b NIRV).

David said to the Philistine, "You come against me with sword and spear and javelin, but I come against you in the name of the LORD Almighty" (1 Sm 17:45).

All of them wearing the sword, all experienced in battle, each with his sword at his side, prepared for the terrors of the night (Sg 3:8).

Say to God, "How awesome are your deeds! So great is your power that your enemies cringe before you" (Ps 66:3).

He made my mouth like a sharpened sword, in the shadow of his hand he hid me; he made me into a polished arrow and concealed me in his quiver (Is 49:2).

The sword is appointed to be polished, to be grasped with the hand; it is sharpened and polished, made ready for the hand of the slayer (Ez 21:11).

Live by the Spirit. The fruit of the Spirit is love, joy, peace, patience, kindness, goodness, faithfulness, gentleness and self-control. Let us keep in step with the Spirit (Gal 5:16, 22, 25).

For the word of God is living and active. Sharper than any double-edged sword, it penetrates even to dividing soul and spirit, joints and marrow; it judges the thoughts and attitudes of the heart (Heb 4:12).

In his right hand he held seven stars, and out of his mouth came a sharp double-edged sword. His face was like the sun shining in all its brilliance (Rv 1:16).

They overcame him by the blood of the Lamb and by the word of their testimony (Rv 12:11).

7. The LORD Watches Your Back

Where you cannot see, where you are most vulnerable; you are protected!

Then the angel of God, who had been traveling in front of Israel's army, withdrew and went behind them (Ex 14:19a).

Have you not put a hedge around him and his household and everything he has? (Jb 1:10a).

You have not handed me over to the enemy but have set my feet in a spacious place (Ps 31:8).

Let those who love the LORD hate evil, for he guards the lives of his faithful ones and delivers them from the hand of the wicked (Ps 97:10).

The LORD is with me; I will not be afraid. What can man do to me? The LORD is with me; he is my helper. I will look in triumph on my enemies (Ps 118:6–7).

The LORD will keep you from all harm—he will watch over your life (Ps 121:7).

But you will not leave in haste or go in flight; for the LORD will go before you, the God of Israel will be your rear guard (Is 52:12).

Then your light will break forth like the dawn, and your healing will quickly appear; then your righteousness will go before you, and the glory of the LORD will be your rear guard (Is 58:8).

8. Shout the Victory! Raise the Banner!

May he send you help from his sanctuary and grant you support from Zion. May he remember all your sacrifices. May he give you the desires of your heart and make all our plans succeed. We will shout for joy when we are victorious and will lift up our banners in the name of our God. May the LORD grant our request (Ps 20:2–5).

Evening, morning and noon I cry out in my distress, and he hears my voice. He ransoms me unharmed from the battle waged against me even though many oppose me (Ps 55:17–18).

He has taken me to the banquet hall, and his banner over me is love (Sg 2:4).

Raise a banner on a bare hilltop, shout to them; beckon to them to enter the gates of the nobles (Is 13:2).

All you people of the world, you who live on the earth, when a banner is raised on the mountains, you will see it, and when a trumpet sounds, you will hear it (Is 18:3).

ARMOR

The LORD will fight for you; you need only to be still.
Exodus 14:14

Daily Prayer
Pages/Journal
Entries

Daily

(My Personal Example)

Praise and Proclaim, Offer Thanks, Search and Confess,
Listen, Apply Armor

Date 1/17/08

Personal Needs

Trust in the LORD with all your heart and lean not on your own understanding; in all your ways acknowledge him and he will direct your paths. (Prv 3:5–6)

LORD, I seek your will in these next steps. You tell me to ask, seek, and knock. I am asking for your will, seeking your direction, and knocking on different doors. Please open the best door for me to publish this book when the time is right.

Immediate Family

May _____ pursue righteousness, godliness, faith, love, endurance, and gentleness. (1 Tm 6:11)

May my children and husband, (list by name and put in the prayer above. Add anything specific.) Give my children an awareness of your presence today.

My Activities Today

Now to him who is able to do immeasurably more than we all we ask or imagine, according to his power that is at work within us, to him be the glory. (Eph 3:20)

Use me, LORD, as I go about my day. Bless the work of my hands and my mind with instruction for the details of this book. Open the doors of opportunity.

Special Concern

"You, who daily bear our burdens, encourage the marriages that are hurting, P&J, B&C. Bring your love and reconciliation." (Ps 68:19)

Missionary

Protect Kelly and Ralph. Help them not to fear, but to share the gospel in power.

Ask and it will be given to you; seek and you will find;
knock and the door will be opened to you.
Matthew 7:7

(My Personal Example)

4/7/07

Dear LORD,

Thank you for the grace given me in Christ Jesus. For in him I have been enriched in every way—Therefore, I do not lack any spiritual gift as I eagerly wait for our Lord Jesus. He will keep me strong to the end . . . God who has called me into fellowship with his Son is faithful! (1 Cor 1:7, 8a, 9)

Thank you, LORD, for leading me to these verses today as a reminder that you do all things through me. As I attempt to finish this book, you have given me much grace. You have enriched me in every way that I do not lack any spiritual gift to complete this. Because you are faithful! I must choose to trust and believe. I needed this boost of confidence!

As we returned from vacation with the kids, it was all about making our dreams come true. My heart was moved as I watched 71,000 people at the amusement park. The possibility of that many people getting this book in their hands and using it, actually praying . . . that is my dream come true! For God to use it and encourage people into a new or deeper relationship with him, increasing their prayer lives, building their faith, to help build up his kingdom . . . that would delight my heart!

Give me clarity, focus, and the ability to hear your voice and what you want in this book. I so desire that every pen stroke, every word, and thought please you. Bless those who have read the book and given their time to give me feedback. Give them abundant time back. Give them joy! Thank you for calling me into fellowship with your Son. There is no greater gift of grace! In return I give this gift, this prayer journal, this offering of sacrifice. I lay it at the foot of the cross, as well as, my life. Take it, LORD, not my will, but yours be done.

In the precious name of Jesus,

I love you!

Sarah

DAILY PRAYER

Praise and Proclaim, Offer Thanks, Search and Confess,
Listen, Apply Armor

Date _____

DAILY

Personal Needs

Which of you, if his son asks for bread, will give him a stone? Or if he asks for a fish, will give him a snake? If you, then, though you are evil, know how to give good gifts to your children, how much more will your Father in heaven give good gifts to those who ask him! (Mt 7:9–10)

_____

_____

_____

Immediate Family

By your word keep _____ from paths of the destroyer so his/her feet do not slip. (Ps 17:4 NKJV)

_____

_____

Activities for Today

LORD, help me bring you glory on earth by completing the work you gave me to do. (Jn 17:4)

_____

_____

Special Concern

_____

_____

Missionary

_____

_____

GRACE FOR THE JOURNEY

He opened the doors of the heavens; he rained down manna
for the people to eat, he gave them the grain of heaven.
Psalm 78:23–24

DAILY PRAYER

Praise and Proclaim, Offer Thanks, Search and Confess, Listen, Apply Armor

Date _____

Personal Needs

Hear, O LORD, and answer me, for I am poor and needy. Guard my life, for I am devoted to you. You are my God; save your servant who trusts in you. (Ps 86:1–2)

_____

_____

_____

Immediate Family

Teach _____ your way, O LORD, and to walk in your truth; give them an undivided heart, that they may fear your name. (Ps 86:11)

_____

_____

My Activities Today

Here, in the presence of the LORD, my God, my family and I will eat and rejoice in everything we have put our hand to, because the LORD, my God has blessed us. (Dt 12:7)

_____

_____

Special Concern

_____

_____

Missionary

_____

_____

GRACE FOR THE JOURNEY

It is the bread the LORD has given you to eat. This is what the LORD has commanded: "Each one is to gather as much as he needs . . . each morning."
Exodus 16:15–16, 21

Praise and Proclaim, Offer Thanks, Search and Confess,
Listen, Apply Armor

Date _____

DAILY

Personal Needs

Create in me a pure heart, O God, and renew a steadfast spirit within me. Do not cast me from your presence or take your Holy Spirit from me. Restore to me the joy of your salvation and grant me a willing spirit, to sustain me. (Ps 51:10–12)

_____

_____

_____

Immediate Family

But as for _____, it is good for them to be near God. May they make the Sovereign LORD their refuge; may they tell of all your deeds. (Ps 73:28)

_____

_____

My Activities Today

You guide me with your counsel, and afterwards you will take me into glory. (Ps 73:24)

_____

_____

Special Concern

_____

_____

Missionary

_____

_____

Moses said, "This is what the LORD commands: Take an omer of manna and keep it for generations to come so they can see the bread I gave you."
Exodus 16:32

DAILY PRAYER

Praise and Proclaim, Offer Thanks, Search and Confess, Listen, Apply Armor

Date _____

Personal Needs

LORD, help me be an example of patience in the face of suffering. (Jas 5:10)

_____

_____

_____

Immediate Family

Bring health and healing to _____; heal your people and let them enjoy abundant peace and security. (Jer 33:6)

_____

_____

My Activities Today

LORD, help me stand firm. Let nothing move me. May I always give myself fully to your work, because I know that my labor for you is not in vain. (1 Cor 15:58)

_____

_____

Special Concern

_____

_____

Missionary

_____

_____

When Moses came down from Mount Sinai with the two tablets of the Testimony in his hands, he was not aware that his face was radiant because he had spoken with the LORD.
Exodus 34:29

DAILY PRAYER

Praise and Proclaim, Offer Thanks, Search and Confess, Listen, Apply Armor

Date _____

Personal Needs

May I taste and see that you are good; blessed am I who takes refuge in you. May I fear you, for those who fear you lack nothing. (Ps 34:8–9)

_____

_____

_____

Immediate Family

May your eyes watch over _____ for their good, and bring them back to this land. You build them up and do not tear them down; you plant them and not uproot them. Please give them a heart to know you, that you are the great I AM, the LORD. May they be your people, and you be their God, may _____ return to you with all their hearts. (Jer 24:6–7)

_____

_____

My Activities Today

Search me, O God, and know my heart; test me and know my anxious thoughts. See if there is any offensive way in me, and lead me in the way everlasting. (Ps 139:23–24)

_____

_____

Special Concern

_____

_____

Missionary

_____

_____

Then have them make a sanctuary for me, and I will dwell among them.
Exodus 25:8

DAILY PRAYER

Praise and Proclaim, Offer Thanks, Search and Confess, Listen, Apply Armor

Date _____

Personal Needs

May the words of my mouth and the meditation of my heart be pleasing in your sight, O LORD, my Rock and my Redeemer. (Ps 19:14)

_____

_____

_____

Immediate Family

I pray that out of his glorious riches he may strengthen _____ with power through the Holy Spirit in their inner being, so that Christ may dwell in their heart through faith. And I pray _____ will be rooted and established in love and grasp how deep is the love of Christ. (Eph 3:16–20)

_____

_____

My Activities Today

LORD, help me love others as you have loved me. (Jn 15:12)

_____

_____

Special Concern

_____

_____

Missionary

_____

_____

GRACE FOR THE JOURNEY

I am the LORD your God; consecrate yourselves
and be holy, because I am holy.
Leviticus 11:44a

_____

_____

_____

_____

_____

_____

_____

_____

_____

_____

_____

_____

_____

_____

_____

_____

_____

_____

_____

_____

_____

_____

_____

DAILY PRAYER

Praise and Proclaim, Offer Thanks, Search and Confess, Listen, Apply Armor

Date _____

Personal Needs

LORD, you said if I believe, I will receive whatever I ask in prayer. Help me believe! (Mt 21:22)

_____

_____

_____

Immediate Family

I tell you the truth, if you have faith as small as a mustard seed, you can say to this mountain, "Move from here to there" and it will move. Nothing will be impossible for you. (Mt 17:20)

_____

_____

My Activities Today

Those who trust in the LORD are like Mount Zion, which cannot be shaken but endures forever. (Ps 125:1)

_____

_____

Special Concern

_____

_____

Missionary

_____

_____

Aaron must burn fragrant incense on the altar every morning . . .
He must burn incense again at twilight so incense will burn
regularly before the LORD for generations to come.
Exodus 30:7–8

DAILY PRAYER

**Praise and Proclaim, Offer Thanks, Search and Confess,
Listen, Apply Armor**

DAILY

Date ——————

Personal Needs

How great is the joy in the victories you give! You have granted me
the desires of my heart and have not withheld the request of my lips.
(Ps 21:1b–2)

———————————————————————————

———————————————————————————

———————————————————————————

Immediate Family

The LORD will cause men to hear his majestic voice and will make them
see his arm coming down. (Is 30:30a)

———————————————————————————

———————————————————————————

My Activities Today

If I give all I possess to the poor and surrender my body to the flames, but
have not love, I gain nothing. (1 Cor 13:3)

———————————————————————————

———————————————————————————

Special Concern

———————————————————————————

———————————————————————————

Missionary

———————————————————————————

———————————————————————————

*For the generations to come this burnt offering is to be made
regularly at the entrance to the Tent of Meeting before the
LORD. There I will meet you and speak to you.*
Exodus 29:42

DAILY

DAILY PRAYER

Praise and Proclaim, Offer Thanks, Search and Confess, Listen, Apply Armor

Date _____

Personal Needs

Blessed are they who maintain justice, who constantly do what is right. Remember me, O LORD, when you show favor to your people, come to my aid. (Ps 106:3–4)

_____

_____

_____

Immediate Family

For everything God created is good, and nothing is to be rejected if it is received with thanksgiving because it is consecrated by the word of God and prayer. (1 Tm 4:4)

_____

_____

My Activities Today

I thank Christ Jesus our Lord, who has given me strength, that he considered me faithful, appointing me to his service. (1 Tm 1:12)

_____

_____

Special Concern

_____

_____

Missionary

_____

_____

Make a fragrant blend of incense, the work of a perfumer. It is to be salted and pure and sacred . . . Place it in front of the Testimony in the Tent of Meeting, where I will meet with you. It shall be most holy to you.
Exodus 30:35–36

DAILY

DAILY PRAYER

Praise and Proclaim, Offer Thanks, Search and Confess,
Listen, Apply Armor

Date _____

Personal Needs

Do not withhold your mercy from me, O LORD; may your love and
your truth always protect me. (Ps 40:11)

_____

_____

_____

Immediate Family

For with you is the fountain of life; in your light we see light. (Ps 36:9)

_____

_____

My Activities Today

O LORD, you are my God; . . . for in perfect faithfulness you have done
marvelous things, things planned long ago. (Is 25:1)

_____

_____

Special Concern

_____

_____

Missionary

_____

_____

Perfume and incense bring joy to the heart.
Proverbs 27:9a

DAILY PRAYER

Praise and Proclaim, Offer Thanks, Search and Confess,
Listen, Apply Armor

Date _____

Personal Needs

All the days ordained for me were written in your book before one of
them came to be. (Ps 139:16b)

_____

_____

_____

Immediate Family

If you remain in me and my words remain in you, ask whatever you
wish, and it will be given you. (Jn 15:7)

_____

_____

My Activities Today

May I live for your glory, and bear as much fruit possible, showing myself
to be your disciple. (Jn 15:8a)

_____

_____

Special Concern

_____

_____

Missionary

_____

_____

Behind the second curtain was a room called the Most Holy Place, which had the golden altar of incense and the gold-covered ark of the covenant.
Hebrews 9:3–4a

Praise and Proclaim, Offer Thanks, Search and Confess,
Listen, Apply Armor

Date _____

DAILY

Personal Needs

I will praise you, O LORD my God, with all my heart; I will glorify your name forever. For great is your love toward me; you have delivered me from the depths of the grave. (Ps 86:12–13)

_____

_____

_____

Immediate Family

May _____ trust in the LORD with all his/her heart and lean not on his/her own understanding. (Prv 3:5)

_____

_____

My Activities Today

Turn to me and have mercy on me; grant your strength to your servant. (Ps 86:16a)

_____

_____

Special Concern

_____

_____

Missionary

_____

_____

In the morning you will be filled with bread.
Then you will know that I am the LORD your God.
Exodus 16:12b

_____

_____

_____

_____

_____

_____

_____

_____

_____

_____

_____

_____

_____

_____

_____

_____

_____

_____

_____

_____

_____

_____

DAILY PRAYER

Praise and Proclaim, Offer Thanks, Search and Confess,
Listen, Apply Armor

Date _____

Personal Needs

Have mercy on me, O LORD, for I call to you all day long. Bring joy to your servant, for to you, O LORD, I lift up my soul. (Ps 86:3–4)

_____

_____

_____

Immediate Family

May we honor the LORD with our wealth, with the first fruits of all our crops. (Prv 3:9)

_____

_____

My Activities Today

LORD, you said to cast my cares on you and you will sustain me; you will never let the righteous fall. (Ps 55:22)

_____

_____

Special Concern

_____

_____

Missionary

_____

_____

GRACE FOR THE JOURNEY

May my prayer be set before you like incense; may the lifting up of my hands be like the evening sacrifice.
Psalm 141:2

DAILY PRAYER

Praise and Proclaim, Offer Thanks, Search and Confess,
Listen, Apply Armor

Date _____

Personal Needs

Blessed are those who mourn, for they will be comforted. (Mt 5:4)

_____

_____

_____

Immediate Family

May _____ turn his/her ear to wisdom and apply their heart to understanding and may they search for it as hidden treasure. (Prv 2:2, 4b)

_____

_____

My Activities Today

Help me be strong and courageous and do the work, and not be afraid or discouraged, for you are with me. (1 Chr 28:20a)

_____

_____

Special Concern

_____

_____

Missionary

_____

_____

Write down the revelation and make it plain on tablets so that a herald may run with it. For the revelation awaits an appointed time; it speaks of the end and will not prove false. Though it linger, wait for it; it will certainly come and not delay.
Habakkuk 2:2–3

DAILY

_____

_____

_____

_____

_____

_____

_____

_____

_____

_____

_____

_____

_____

_____

_____

_____

_____

_____

_____

_____

_____

_____

_____

_____

DAILY PRAYER

Praise and Proclaim, Offer Thanks, Search and Confess,
Listen, Apply Armor

Date _____

Personal Needs

You are forgiving and good, O LORD, abounding in love to all who call
to you. (Ps 86:5)

_____

_____

_____

Immediate Family

Praise be to the God and Father of our Lord Jesus Christ, the Father of
compassion and the God of all comfort, comfort us in all our troubles, so
that we can comfort those in any trouble with the comfort we ourselves
have received from God. (2 Cor 1:3–4)

_____

_____

My Activities Today

Through the power of the Holy Spirit who lives in me, help me guard the
precious truth that has been given me. (1 Tm 1:13 NLT)

_____

_____

Special Concern

_____

_____

Missionary

_____

_____

Lift up your heads, O you gates; be lifted up, you ancient doors,
that the King of glory may come in.
Psalm 24:7

DAILY

_____

_____

_____

_____

_____

_____

_____

_____

_____

_____

_____

_____

_____

_____

_____

_____

_____

_____

_____

_____

DAILY PRAYER

Praise and Proclaim, Offer Thanks, Search and Confess, Listen, Apply Armor

Date _____

Personal Needs

By day the LORD directs his love, at night his song is with me—a prayer to the God of my life. (Ps 42:8)

_____

_____

_____

Immediate Family

For the grace of God that brings salvation has appeared to all men. It teaches _____ to say "No" to ungodliness and worldly passions, and to live self-controlled, upright and godly lives in this present age. (Ti 2:11–12)

_____

_____

My Activities Today

LORD give me instruction, as you gave David the plans of all that the Spirit had put in his mind for the temple. (1 Chr 28:12–13)

_____

_____

Special Concern

_____

_____

Missionary

_____

_____

GRACE FOR THE JOURNEY

The priests and the Levites stood to bless the people, and God heard them,
for their prayer reached heaven, his holy dwelling place.
2 Chronicles 30:27

DAILY

DAILY PRAYER

Praise and Proclaim, Offer Thanks, Search and Confess,
Listen, Apply Armor

Date _____

Personal Needs

I run in the path of your commands, for you have set my heart free.
(Ps 119:32)

_____

_____

_____

Immediate Family

May _____ hope in the LORD and renew his/her strength.
(Is 40:31a)

_____

_____

My Activities Today

If I lack wisdom, you tell me to ask you, and you will give generously to
all without finding fault. I ask believing. Remove any doubt. (Jas 1:5–6a)

_____

_____

Special Concern

_____

_____

Missionary

_____

_____

GRACE FOR THE JOURNEY

Better is one day in your courts than a thousand elsewhere;
I would rather be a doorkeeper in the house of my
God than dwell in the tents of the wicked.
Psalm 84:10

DAILY PRAYER

Praise and Proclaim, Offer Thanks, Search and Confess, Listen, Apply Armor

Date ——————————

DAILY

Personal Needs

LORD, if it is encouraging, let me encourage; if it is contributing to the needs of others, let me give generously; if it is leadership, let me govern diligently; if it is showing mercy, let me do it cheerfully. (Rom 12:8)

——————————————————————————————————

——————————————————————————————————

——————————————————————————————————

Immediate Family

May we greet one another with a kiss of love and bring peace to all who are in Christ. (1 Pt 5:14)

——————————————————————————————————

——————————————————————————————————

My Activities Today

If it is possible, as far as it depends on me, help me live at peace with everyone. (Rom 12:18)

——————————————————————————————————

——————————————————————————————————

Special Concern

——————————————————————————————————

——————————————————————————————————

Missionary

——————————————————————————————————

——————————————————————————————————

And I will pour out on the house of David and the inhabitants of Jerusalem a spirit of grace and supplication. They will look on me, the one they have pierced, and they will mourn for him as one mourns for an only child, and grieve bitterly for him as one grieves for a firstborn son.
Zechariah 12:10

DAILY PRAYER

Praise and Proclaim, Offer Thanks, Search and Confess,
Listen, Apply Armor

Date _____

Personal Needs

Let love and faithfulness never leave me; bind them around my neck,
write them on the tablet of my heart. (Prv 3:3)

_____

_____

_____

Immediate Family

It is God who arms _____ with strength and makes his/her way
perfect. (Ps 18:32)

_____

_____

My Activities Today

May I love the LORD my God with all my heart and with all my soul and
with all my strength. (Dt 6:5)

_____

_____

Special Concern

_____

_____

Missionary

_____

_____

*We do have such a high priest, who sat down at the right hand
of the throne of the Majesty in heaven, and who serves in the
sanctuary, the true tabernacle set up by the LORD, not by man.*
Hebrews 8:1b–2

DAILY

DAILY PRAYER

Praise and Proclaim, Offer Thanks, Search and Confess,
Listen, Apply Armor

Date _____

Personal Needs

May integrity and uprightness protect me, because my hope is in you.
(Ps 25:21)

_____

_____

_____

Immediate Family

Though my father and mother forsake me, the LORD will receive me.
(Ps 27:10)

_____

_____

My Activities Today

You guide me with your counsel, and afterward you will take me into
glory. Whom have I in heaven but you? And earth has nothing I desire
besides you. (Ps 73:24–25)

_____

_____

Special Concern

_____

_____

Missionary

_____

_____

We have this hope as an anchor for the soul, firm and secure.
It enters the inner sanctuary behind the curtain, where Jesus, who went
before us, has entered on our behalf. He has become a high priest forever.
Hebrews 6:19–20

DAILY

DAILY PRAYER

Praise and Proclaim, Offer Thanks, Search and Confess, Listen, Apply Armor

Date _____

Personal Needs

One thing I ask of the LORD, this is what I seek: that I may dwell in the house of the LORD all the days of my life, to gaze upon the beauty of the LORD and to seek him in his temple. (Ps 27:4)

_____

_____

_____

Immediate Family

God is not unjust; he will not forget your work and the love you have shown him as you have helped his people and continue to help them. (Heb 6:10)

_____

_____

My Activities Today

Even when I am old and gray, do not forsake me, O God, till I declare your power to the next generation, your might to all who are to come. (Ps 71:18)

_____

_____

Special Concern

_____

_____

Missionary

_____

_____

You welcomed him with rich blessings and placed a crown of pure gold on head. Surely you have granted him with eternal blessings and made him glad with the joy of your presence.
Psalm 21:3, 6

Praise and Proclaim, Offer Thanks, Search and Confess,
Listen, Apply Armor

Date _____

Personal Needs

My soul yearns for you in the night; in the morning my spirit longs for you. (Is 26:9a)

_____

_____

_____

Immediate Family

We do not want _____ to become lazy, but to imitate those who through faith and patience inherit what has been promised. (Heb 6:12)

_____

_____

My Activities Today

LORD, help me forget the former things and not dwell on the past, but see you are doing a new thing! (Is 43:18–19)

_____

_____

Special Concern

_____

_____

Missionary

_____

_____

The LORD bless you and keep you; the LORD make his face shine upon you
and be gracious to you; the LORD turn his face toward
you and give you peace.
Numbers 6:24–26

_____

_____

_____

_____

_____

_____

_____

_____

_____

_____

_____

_____

_____

_____

_____

_____

_____

_____

_____

_____

_____

DAILY PRAYER

Praise and Proclaim, Offer Thanks, Search and Confess, Listen, Apply Armor

DAILY

Date ─────────

Personal Needs

I delight greatly in the LORD; my soul rejoices in my God. For he has clothed me with garments of salvation and arrayed me in a robe of righteousness. (Is 61:10a)

───────────────────────────────

───────────────────────────────

───────────────────────────────

Immediate Family

Heal _____ of a broken heart and bind up their wounds. (Ps 147:3)

───────────────────────────────

───────────────────────────────

My Activities Today

Do not let my heart be troubled. May I trust in you. (Jn 14:1)

───────────────────────────────

───────────────────────────────

Special Concern

───────────────────────────────

───────────────────────────────

Missionary

───────────────────────────────

───────────────────────────────

*He appointed some of the Levites to minister before the ark of the LORD,
to make petition, to give thanks, and to praise the LORD, the God of Israel.*
1 Chronicles 16:4

DAILY PRAYER

Praise and Proclaim, Offer Thanks, Search and Confess, Listen, Apply Armor

Date _____

Personal Needs

Come, my people, enter my chambers and shut the door behind you. Hide yourselves for a little while. (Is 26:20)

_____

_____

_____

Immediate Family

As aliens and strangers in the world, help _____ to abstain from sinful desires, which war against his/her soul. Help him/her live such good lives among the pagans that, though they accuse _____ of doing wrong, they may see his/her good deeds and glorify God on the day he visits us. (1 Pt 2:11–12)

_____

_____

My Activities Today

I have revealed and saved and proclaimed . . . "You are my witnesses," declares the LORD, "that I am God." (Is 43:12)

_____

_____

Special Concern

_____

_____

Missionary

_____

_____

GRACE FOR THE JOURNEY

For this reason he had to be made like his brothers in every way,
in order that he might become a merciful and faithful high priest in service
to God, and that he might make atonement for the sins of the people.
Hebrews 2:17

DAILY PRAYER

Praise and Proclaim, Offer Thanks, Search and Confess, Listen, Apply Armor

Date _____

Personal Needs

I remember the days of long ago; I meditate on all your works and consider what your hands have done. I spread out my hands to you; my soul thirsts for you like a parched land. (Ps 143:5–6)

_____

_____

_____

Immediate Family

Let everyone who is godly pray to you while you may be found. Surely when the mighty waters rise they will not reach _____. (Ps 32:6)

_____

_____

My Activities Today

Praise be to the LORD, for he showed his wonderful love to me. (Ps 31:21a)

_____

_____

Special Concern

_____

_____

Missionary

_____

_____

GRACE FOR THE JOURNEY

It is good for our hearts to be strengthened by grace.
Hebrews 13:9b

DAILY PRAYER

Praise and Proclaim, Offer Thanks, Search and Confess, Listen, Apply Armor

Date _____

Personal Needs

Let the morning bring me word of your unfailing love for I have put my trust in you. Show me the way I should go, for to you I lift up my soul. (Ps 143:8)

_____

_____

_____

Immediate Family

And my God will meet all your needs according to his glorious riches in Christ Jesus. (Phil 4:19)

_____

_____

My Activities Today

LORD, you promise as I seek you to deliver me from all my fears. (Ps 34:4)

_____

_____

Special Concern

_____

_____

Missionary

_____

_____

Rend your hearts and not your garments.
Return to the LORD your God, for he is gracious and compassionate.
Joel 2:13

DAILY PRAYER

Praise and Proclaim, Offer Thanks, Search and Confess,
Listen, Apply Armor

Date _____

Personal Needs

Blessed am I who has believed that what the LORD has said to me will
be accomplished! (Lk 1:45)

_____

_____

_____

Immediate Family

For he himself is our peace, who has made the two one and has destroyed
the barrier, the dividing wall of hostility. (Eph 2:14)

_____

_____

My Activities Today

LORD, you establish peace for us; all that we have accomplished you
have done for us. (Is 26:12)

_____

_____

Special Concern

_____

_____

Missionary

_____

_____

Look to the LORD; seek his face always. Remember the wonders he has done.
Psalm 105:4–5

DAILY PRAYER

Praise and Proclaim, Offer Thanks, Search and Confess, Listen, Apply Armor

Date _____

Personal Needs

Thank you LORD, that you chose me to be in Christ before the creation of the world to be holy and blameless in your sight. In love you predestined me to be adopted as your child in accordance with your pleasure and will. (Eph 1:4–5)

_____

_____

_____

Immediate Family

I pray also that the eyes of _____'s heart may be enlightened in order that he/she may know the hope to which he has called them, the riches of his glorious inheritance in the saints, and his incomparably great power for us who believe. (Eph 1:18–19)

_____

_____

My Activities Today

In you, I was also chosen, according to your plan. Thank you, LORD, you work out everything to the conformity of your purpose and will. (Eph 1:11)

_____

_____

Special Concern

_____

_____

Missionary

_____

_____

Yours, O LORD, is the greatness and the power and the glory and the majesty and the splendor, for everything in heaven and earth is yours. Yours is the kingdom.
1 Chronicles 29:11

DAILY

DAILY PRAYER

**Praise and Proclaim, Offer Thanks, Search and Confess,
Listen, Apply Armor**

Date _____

Personal Needs

He has made me competent as ministers of a new covenant—not of
the letter but of the Spirit; for the letter kills, but the Spirit gives life.
(2 Cor 3:6)

_____

_____

_____

Immediate Family

Do not let this Book of the Law depart from _____'s mouth; may
he/she meditate on it day and night, so that he/she may be careful to do
everything written in it. Then he/she will be prosperous and successful.
(Josh 1:8)

_____

_____

My Activities Today

May I be strong and courageous. May I not be terrified; not be discouraged,
for the LORD, my God, will be with me wherever I go. (Josh 1:9)

_____

_____

Special Concern

_____

_____

Missionary

_____

_____

Such confidence as this is ours through Christ before God.
Not that we are competent in ourselves to claim anything
for ourselves, but our competence comes from God.
2 Corinthians 3:4–5

Praise and Proclaim, Offer Thanks, Search and Confess,
Listen, Apply Armor

DAILY

Date _____

Personal Needs

You have made known to me the path of life; you will fill me with joy in your presence, with eternal pleasures at your right hand. (Ps 16:11)

_____

_____

_____

Immediate Family

A father to the fatherless, a defender to the widows, is God in his holy dwelling. God sets the lonely in families, he leads forth the prisoners with singing; but the rebellious live in a sun scorched land. (Ps 68:5–6)

_____

_____

My Activities Today

LORD, whatever I do, whether in word or deed, may I do it all in the name of the Lord Jesus, giving thanks to God the Father through him, working at it with all my heart, as working for the Lord, not for men. (Col 3:17, 23)

_____

_____

Special Concern

_____

_____

Missionary

_____

_____

For the LORD will be your confidence.
Proverbs 3:26a

_____

_____

_____

_____

_____

_____

_____

_____

_____

_____

_____

_____

_____

_____

_____

_____

_____

_____

_____

_____

_____

_____

_____

_____

DAILY PRAYER

Praise and Proclaim, Offer Thanks, Search and Confess, Listen, Apply Armor

Date _____

Personal Needs

God called to him from within the bush, "Moses! Moses!" And Moses said, "Here I am." May I have a willing heart like Moses. (Ex 3:4)

_____

_____

_____

Immediate Family

May _____'s path be like the first gleam of dawn, shining ever brighter till the full light of day. (Prv 4:18)

_____

_____

My Activities Today

LORD, I'll go where you send me. You promise to help me speak and teach me what to say. (Ex 4:12)

_____

_____

Special Concern

_____

_____

Missionary

_____

_____

*This then is how we know that we belong to the truth,
and how we set our hearts at rest in his presence.*
1 John 3:19

DAILY PRAYER

Praise and Proclaim, Offer Thanks, Search and Confess,
Listen, Apply Armor

Date _____

Personal Needs

What must I do to inherit eternal life? . . . Come follow me. (Lk 18:18b, 22b)

_____

_____

_____

Immediate Family

Glorify the LORD with me; let us exalt his name together. I sought the LORD, and he answered me; he delivered me from all my fears. (Ps 34:3–4)

_____

_____

My Activities Today

LORD, help me be sharp to serve, for physical training is of some value, but godliness has value for all things, holding promise for both the present life and the life to come. (1 Tm 4:8)

_____

_____

Special Concern

_____

_____

Missionary

_____

_____

The LORD said . . ., "I am your share and your inheritance."
Numbers 18:20

_____

_____
_____
_____
_____
_____
_____
_____
_____
_____
_____
_____
_____
_____
_____
_____
_____
_____
_____
_____
_____

Praise and Proclaim, Offer Thanks, Search and Confess,
Listen, Apply Armor

Date _____

DAILY

Personal Needs

When I consider your heavens, the work of your fingers, the moon and the stars, which you have set in place, what is man that you are mindful of him, the son of man that you care for him? You made him a little lower than the heavenly beings and crowned him with glory and honor. (Ps 8:3–5)

_____

_____

_____

Immediate Family

Love the LORD all his saints! The LORD preserves the faithful, but the proud he pays back in full. (Ps 31:23)

_____

_____

My Activities Today

LORD, may our plans be your plans, if our purpose or activity is of human origin, it will fail. (Acts 5:38)

_____

_____

Special Concern

_____

_____

Missionary

_____

_____

One thing I ask of the LORD, this is what I seek: that I may dwell in the house of the LORD all the days of my life, to gaze upon the beauty of the LORD and to seek him in his temple.
Psalm 27:4

DAILY PRAYER

Praise and Proclaim, Offer Thanks, Search and Confess, Listen, Apply Armor

Date _____

Personal Needs

Here I am, I have come to do your will. (Heb 10:9a)

_____

_____

_____

Immediate Family

LORD, give strength to _____ and bless them with peace. (Ps 29:11)

_____

_____

My Activities Today

I know my God, that you test the heart and are pleased with integrity. (1 Chr 29:17a)

_____

_____

Special Concern

_____

_____

Missionary

_____

_____

97

O you who hear prayer, to you all men will come.
Psalm 65:2

Praise and Proclaim, Offer Thanks, Search and Confess,
Listen, Apply Armor

Date _____

DAILY

Personal Needs

Come quickly to help me, O LORD my Savior. (Ps 38:22)

_____

_____

_____

Immediate Family

LORD, let us be salt to our families and live at peace with each other.
(Mk 9:50)

_____

_____

My Activities Today

LORD, help me keep my head today in all situations, to endure hardship,
and do the work of an evangelist. (2 Tm 4:5)

_____

_____

Special Concern

_____

_____

Missionary

_____

_____

These I bring to my holy mountain and give them joy in my house of prayer.
Isaiah 56:7a

Praise and Proclaim, Offer Thanks, Search and Confess,
Listen, Apply Armor

Date _____

Personal Needs

But he gives us more grace. That is why Scripture says: "God opposes the proud but gives grace to the humble." Submit yourselves, then, to God. Resist the devil, and he will flee from you. (Jas 4:6–7)

_____

_____

_____

Immediate Family

May _____ develop a self confidence this is rooted in the realization that they are God's workmanship, created in Christ Jesus to do good works which God prepared in advance for them to do. (Eph 2:10)

_____

_____

My Activities Today

Help me pay attention to the ministry I have received from the LORD so I can accomplish it. (Col 4:17 HCSB)

_____

_____

Special Concern

_____

_____

Missionary

_____

_____

So do not throw away your confidence; it will be richly rewarded. You need to persevere so that when you have done the will of God, you will receive what he has promised. For in just a very little while, "He who is coming will come and will not delay. But my righteous one will live by faith."
Hebrews 10:35–38a

DAILY PRAYER

Praise and Proclaim, Offer Thanks, Search and Confess,
Listen, Apply Armor

Date _____

Personal Needs

LORD, direct my heart into God's love and Christ's perseverance.
(2 Thes 3:5)

_____

_____

_____

Immediate Family

May our Lord Jesus Christ himself and God our Father, who loved us
and by grace gave us eternal encouragement and good hope, encourage
_____s' heart and strengthen them in every good deed and word.
(2 Thes 2:16–17)

_____

_____

My Activities Today

Give me grace today to preach the word in season and out of season, . . .
with great patience and careful instruction. (2 Tm 4:2)

_____

_____

Special Concern

_____

_____

Missionary

_____

_____

GRACE FOR THE JOURNEY

Do not be in a hurry to leave the king's presence . . .
Ecclesiastes 8:3

DAILY PRAYER

Praise and Proclaim, Offer Thanks, Search and Confess, Listen, Apply Armor

Date _____

Personal Needs

LORD, thank you for your promise to give me peace at all times and in every way. (2 Thes 3:16)

_____

_____

_____

Immediate Family

Thank you for _____, that their faith is growing more and more, and the love we have for each other is increasing. (2 Thes 1:3)

_____

_____

My Activities Today

I thank Christ Jesus our Lord, who has given me strength, that he considered me faithful appointing me to this service. (1 Tm 1:12)

_____

_____

Special Concern

_____

_____

Missionary

_____

_____

The eyes of the LORD are on the righteous and his ears are attentive to their cry;
the righteous cry out, and the LORD hears them; he delivers them from all their
troubles. The LORD is close to the brokenhearted and saves
those who are crushed in spirit.
Psalm 34:15, 17–18

DAILY

DAILY PRAYER

Praise and Proclaim, Offer Thanks, Search and Confess, Listen, Apply Armor

Date _____

Personal Needs

For I am ready to be poured out like a drink offering . . . I have fought the good fight, I have finished the race, I have kept the faith. Now there is in store for me a crown of righteousness. (2 Tm 4:6–8a)

_____

_____

_____

Immediate Family

Thank you that you gave yourself to redeem _____ from all wickedness and to purify them for yourself as your very own, eager to do what is good. (Ti 2:14)

_____

_____

My Activities Today

May I, who claim to know you God, not deny you by my actions. (Ti 1:16)

_____

_____

Special Concern

_____

_____

Missionary

_____

_____

In the time of my favor I will answer you, and in the day of salvation I will help you; I will keep you and will make you to be a covenant for the people, to restore the land . . . to say to the captives, "Come out," and to those in darkness, "Be free!"
Isaiah 49:8–9

DAILY

Praise and Proclaim, Offer Thanks, Search and Confess,
Listen, Apply Armor

Date _____

DAILY

Personal Needs

May God count me worthy of his calling and that by his power he may
fulfill every good purpose of mine and every act prompted by my faith. We
pray this so the name of our Lord Jesus may be glorified . . . according to the
grace of our God and the Lord Jesus Christ. (2 Thes 1:11–12)

_____

_____

_____

Immediate Family

We ought always to thank God for you, brothers loved by the Lord,
because from the beginning God chose you, to be saved through the
sanctifying work of the Spirit and through belief in the truth. He called
you to this through our gospel, that you might share in the glory of our
Lord Jesus Christ. (2 Thes 2:13–14)

_____

_____

My Activities Today

LORD, you are faithful. Thank you that you promised to strengthen and
protect me from the evil one. (2 Thes 3:3)

_____

_____

Special Concern

_____

_____

Missionary

_____

_____

Wash me, and I will be whiter than snow.
Psalm 51:7

DAILY PRAYER

Praise and Proclaim, Offer Thanks, Search and Confess,
Listen, Apply Armor

Date _____

Personal Needs

God, you did not call me to be impure, but to live a holy life. If I reject this, forgive me, for I am rejecting you who gives me the Holy Spirit. (1 Thes 4:7–8)

_____

_____

_____

Immediate Family

May God, himself, the God of peace, sanctify _____ through and through. May his/her whole spirit, soul and body be kept blameless at the coming of our Lord Jesus Christ. (1 Thes 5:23)

_____

_____

My Activities Today

Help me to make it my ambition to lead a quiet life, mind my own business and work well with my hands so that my daily life may win the respect of outsiders. (1 Thes 4:11–12a)

_____

_____

Special Concern

_____

_____

Missionary

_____

_____

GRACE FOR THE JOURNEY

*Even now my witness is in heaven; my advocate is on high. My
intercessor is my friend as my eyes pour out tears to God; on behalf
of man he pleads with God as a man pleads for his friend.*
Job 16:19–21

Praise and Proclaim, Offer Thanks, Search and Confess,
Listen, Apply Armor

Date _____

DAILY

Personal Needs

Many are the plans in my heart, but it is your purpose that prevails.
(Prv 19:21)

_____

_____

_____

Immediate Family

Yet to all who received him, to those who believed in his name, he
gave the right to become children of God—children born not of natural
descent, nor of human decision or a husband's will, but born of God.
Open _____'s heart to receive Jesus. (Jn 1:12)

_____

_____

My Activities Today

By your grace, LORD, give me your wisdom to gain patience and give you
glory by overlooking an offense. (Prv 19:11)

_____

_____

Special Concern

_____

_____

Missionary

_____

_____

Therefore, if anyone is in Christ, he is a new creation;
the old has gone, the new has come!
All this is from God, who reconciled us to himself through Christ
and gave us the ministry of reconciliation.
2 Corinthians 5:17–18

DAILY

DAILY PRAYER

Praise and Proclaim, Offer Thanks, Search and Confess,
Listen, Apply Armor

Date ————————

Personal Needs

LORD, help me listen and obey for you give wisdom, and from your mouth come knowledge and understanding. (Prv 2:6)

————————————————————————————

————————————————————————————

————————————————————————————

Immediate Family

For this reason, since the day we heard about you, we have not stopped praying for you and asking God to fill you with the knowledge of his will through all spiritual wisdom and understanding. (Col 1:9)

————————————————————————————

————————————————————————————

My Activities Today

LORD, I am coming, and choosing to follow you. Make me a fisher of men. (Mt 4:19)

————————————————————————————

————————————————————————————

Special Concern

————————————————————————————

————————————————————————————

Missionary

————————————————————————————

————————————————————————————

My eyes will be on the faithful in the land, that they may dwell with me;
he whose walk is blameless will minister to me.
Psalm 101:6

DAILY

_____

_____

_____

_____

_____

_____

_____

_____

_____

_____

_____

_____

_____

_____

_____

_____

_____

_____

_____

_____

_____

_____

_____

DAILY PRAYER

Praise and Proclaim, Offer Thanks, Search and Confess, Listen, Apply Armor

Date _____

Personal Needs

May I not be negligent now, for you have chosen me to stand before you and serve you, to minister before you and to burn incense—to offer prayers. (2 Chr 29:11)

_____

_____

_____

Immediate Family

God you are good, a refuge in times of trouble. You care for _____ who trusts in you. (Nah 1:7)

_____

_____

My Activities Today

My words come from an upright heart; my lips sincerely speak what I know. The Spirit of God has made me; the breath of the Almighty gives me life. (Jb 33:3–4)

_____

_____

Special Concern

_____

_____

Missionary

_____

_____

The end of all things is near. Therefore, be clear minded
and self controlled so that you can pray.
1 Peter 4:7

Praise and Proclaim, Offer Thanks, Search and Confess,
Listen, Apply Armor

Date _____

DAILY

Personal Needs   Scripture   Hebrews 2:1

_____
_____
_____
_____

Immediate Family   Scripture   Philemon 1:4–7

_____
_____
_____

My Activities Today   Scripture   Hebrews 2:18

_____
_____
_____

Special Concern

_____
_____
_____

Missionary

_____
_____
_____

Among those who approach me I will show myself holy.
Leviticus 10:3a

_____

_____

_____

_____

_____

_____

_____

_____

_____

_____

_____

_____

_____

_____

_____

_____

_____

_____

_____

_____

_____

_____

_____

_____

DAILY PRAYER

Praise and Proclaim, Offer Thanks, Search and Confess,
Listen, Apply Armor

Date ─────────

DAILY

Personal Needs   Scripture   Titus 3:8

_____
_____
_____
_____

Immediate Family   Scripture   Titus 3:5–6

_____
_____
_____

My Activities Today   Scripture   Titus 3:9

_____
_____
_____

Special Concern

_____
_____
_____

Missionary

_____
_____
_____

Yet the LORD longs to be gracious to you . . . blessed are those who wait for him.
How gracious he will be when you cry for help!
As soon as he hears, he will answer you.
Isaiah 30:18, 19b

DAILY

DAILY PRAYER

Praise and Proclaim, Offer Thanks, Search and Confess,
Listen, Apply Armor

Date _____

Personal Needs Scripture <u>Romans 5:1–2</u>

_____

_____

_____

_____

Immediate Family Scripture <u>Acts 20:32</u>

_____

_____

_____

My Activities Today Scripture <u>Romans 5:3–5</u>

_____

_____

_____

Special Concern

_____

_____

_____

Missionary

_____

_____

_____

From the fullness of his grace we have all received one blessing after another.
John 1:16

DAILY

DAILY PRAYER

Praise and Proclaim, Offer Thanks, Search and Confess,
Listen, Apply Armor

Date _____

Personal Needs   Scripture   <u>1 Chronicles 28:9</u>

_____

_____

_____

_____

Immediate Family   Scripture   <u>Ezekiel 36:25–29</u>

_____

_____

_____

My Activities Today   Scripture   <u>1 Chronicles 28:20</u>

_____

_____

_____

Special Concern

_____

_____

_____

Missionary

_____

_____

_____

Come, all you who are thirsty, come to the waters . . . Come . . . without money and without cost. Why spend money on what is not bread, and your labor on what does not satisfy. Listen, listen to me, and eat what is good, and your soul will delight in the richest of fare.
Isaiah 55:1–2

DAILY PRAYER

Praise and Proclaim, Offer Thanks, Search and Confess,
Listen, Apply Armor

Date _____

Personal Needs   Scripture _____

_____

_____

_____

_____

Immediate Family   Scripture _____

_____

_____

_____

My Activities Today   Scripture _____

_____

_____

_____

Special Concern

_____

_____

_____

Missionary

_____

_____

_____

Dear friends, if our hearts do not condemn us, we have confidence before God and receive from him anything we ask, because we obey his commands and do what pleases him. And this is his command: to believe in the name of his Son, Jesus Christ, and to love one another as he commanded us.
1 John 3:21–23

DAILY

DAILY PRAYER

Praise and Proclaim, Offer Thanks, Search and Confess,
Listen, Apply Armor

Date _____

DAILY

Personal Needs   Scripture   _____

_____

_____

_____

_____

Immediate Family   Scripture   _____

_____

_____

_____

My Activities Today   Scripture   _____

_____

_____

Special Concern

_____

_____

_____

Missionary

_____

_____

_____

As for me, I will continue beholding your face in righteousness
(rightness, justice, and right standing with you); I shall be
fully satisfied, when I awake [to find myself] beholding your
form [and having sweet communion with you].
Psalm 17:15 AMP

DAILY

_____

_____

_____

_____

_____

_____

_____

_____

_____

_____

_____

_____

_____

_____

_____

_____

_____

_____

_____

_____

DAILY PRAYER

Praise and Proclaim, Offer Thanks, Search and Confess,
Listen, Apply Armor

Date _____

Personal Needs   Scripture _____

_____

_____

_____

Immediate Family   Scripture _____

_____

_____

My Activities Today   Scripture _____

_____

_____

Special Concern

_____

_____

_____

Missionary

_____

_____

_____

This is love: not that we loved God, but that he loved us
and sent his Son as an atoning sacrifice for our sins.
1 John 4:10

DAILY

_____

_____

_____

_____

_____

_____

_____

_____

_____

_____

_____

_____

_____

_____

_____

_____

_____

_____

_____

_____

DAILY PRAYER

Praise and Proclaim, Offer Thanks, Search and Confess, Listen, Apply Armor

Date _____

Personal Needs   Scripture _____

_____

_____

_____

_____

Immediate Family   Scripture _____

_____

_____

_____

My Activities Today   Scripture _____

_____

_____

_____

Special Concern

_____

_____

_____

Missionary

_____

_____

_____

You have made known to me the path of life; you fill me with
joy in your presence with eternal pleasures at your right hand.
Psalm 16:11

DAILY PRAYER

Praise and Proclaim, Offer Thanks, Search and Confess,
Listen, Apply Armor

Date _____

Personal Needs   Scripture   _____

_____

_____

_____

_____

Immediate Family   Scripture   _____

_____

_____

_____

My Activities Today   Scripture   _____

_____

_____

_____

Special Concern

_____

_____

_____

Missionary

_____

_____

_____

135

For we know the grace of our Lord Jesus Christ, that though he was rich,
yet for your sakes he became poor, so that you
through his poverty might become rich.
2 Corinthians 8:9

DAILY

_____

DAILY PRAYER

Praise and Proclaim, Offer Thanks, Search and Confess,
Listen, Apply Armor

Date _____

Personal Needs   Scripture   _____

_____

_____

_____

_____

Immediate Family   Scripture   _____

_____

_____

_____

My Activities Today   Scripture   _____

_____

_____

_____

Special Concern

_____

_____

_____

Missionary

_____

_____

_____

137

Come near to God and he will come near to you.
Wash your hands, you sinners, and purify your hearts . . .
James 4:8

DAILY PRAYER

Praise and Proclaim, Offer Thanks, Search and Confess,
Listen, Apply Armor

Date _____

Personal Needs   Scripture   _____

_____

_____

_____

_____

Immediate Family   Scripture   _____

_____

_____

_____

My Activities Today   Scripture   _____

_____

_____

_____

Special Concern

_____

_____

_____

Missionary

_____

_____

_____

But you are a chosen people, a royal priesthood, a holy nation, a people belonging to God, that you may declare the praises of him who called you out of darkness into his wonderful light.
1 Peter 2:9

DAILY PRAYER

Praise and Proclaim, Offer Thanks, Search and Confess,
Listen, Apply Armor

Date _____

Personal Needs   Scripture _____

_____

_____

_____

_____

Immediate Family   Scripture _____

_____

_____

_____

My Activities Today   Scripture _____

_____

_____

_____

Special Concern

_____

_____

_____

Missionary

_____

_____

_____

Who is he that condemns? Christ Jesus, who died—more than that, who was raised to life—is at the right hand of God and is also interceding for us.
Romans 8:34

DAILY

DAILY PRAYER

Praise and Proclaim, Offer Thanks, Search and Confess,
Listen, Apply Armor

Date _____

Personal Needs   Scripture   _____

_____

_____

_____

_____

Immediate Family   Scripture   _____

_____

_____

_____

My Activities Today   Scripture   _____

_____

_____

_____

Special Concern

_____

_____

_____

Missionary

_____

_____

_____

Come, O house of Jacob, let us walk in the light of the LORD.
Isaiah 2:5

DAILY PRAYER

Praise and Proclaim, Offer Thanks, Search and Confess,
Listen, Apply Armor

Date _____

Personal Needs   Scripture _____

_____

_____

_____

_____

Immediate Family   Scripture _____

_____

_____

_____

My Activities Today   Scripture _____

_____

_____

_____

Special Concern

_____

_____

_____

Missionary

_____

_____

_____

145

The LORD would speak to Moses face to face, as a man speaks with his friend.
Exodus 33:11

Prison Book Project
P. O. Box 1146
Sharpes, Fl. 32959

Praise and Proclaim, Offer Thanks, Search and Confess,
Listen, Apply Armor

DAILY

Date _____

Personal Needs   Scripture _____

_____

_____

_____

_____

Immediate Family   Scripture _____

_____

_____

_____

My Activities Today   Scripture _____

_____

_____

_____

Special Concern

_____

_____

_____

Missionary

_____

_____

_____

May my prayer come before you; turn your ear to my cry.
For my soul is full of trouble . . .
Psalm 88:2–3a

DAILY PRAYER

Praise and Proclaim, Offer Thanks, Search and Confess,
Listen, Apply Armor

Date _____

Personal Needs   Scripture   _____

_____

_____

_____

_____

Immediate Family   Scripture   _____

_____

_____

_____

My Activities Today   Scripture   _____

_____

_____

_____

Special Concern

_____

_____

_____

Missionary

_____

_____

_____

GRACE FOR THE JOURNEY

Let us draw near to God with a sincere heart in full assurance of faith, having our hearts sprinkled to cleanse us from a guilty conscience and having our bodies washed with pure water.
Hebrews 10:22

DAILY PRAYER

Praise and Proclaim, Offer Thanks, Search and Confess,
Listen, Apply Armor

Date _____

Personal Needs   Scripture   _____

_____

_____

_____

_____

Immediate Family   Scripture   _____

_____

_____

_____

My Activities Today   Scripture   _____

_____

_____

_____

Special Concern

_____

_____

_____

Missionary

_____

_____

_____

Jesus said to them, "I tell you the truth, it is not Moses who has given you the bread from heaven, but it is my Father who gives you the true bread from heaven." Then Jesus declared, "I am the bread of life. He who comes to me will never go hungry, and he who believes in me will never be thirsty."
John 6:32, 35

_____

_____

_____

_____

_____

_____

_____

_____

_____

_____

_____

_____

_____

_____

_____

_____

_____

_____

_____

_____

_____

_____

_____

DAILY PRAYER

Praise and Proclaim, Offer Thanks, Search and Confess,
Listen, Apply Armor

Date _____

Personal Needs   Scripture _____

_____

_____

_____

_____

Immediate Family   Scripture _____

_____

_____

_____

My Activities Today   Scripture _____

_____

_____

_____

Special Concern

_____

_____

_____

Missionary

_____

_____

_____

Even the sparrow has found a home, and the swallow a nest for herself,
where she may have her young—a place near your altar,
O LORD Almighty, my King and my God.
Blessed are those who dwell in your house;
they are ever praising you.
Psalm 84:3–4

DAILY PRAYER

Praise and Proclaim, Offer Thanks, Search and Confess,
Listen, Apply Armor

Date _____

DAILY

Personal Needs   Scripture   _____

_____

_____

_____

_____

Immediate Family   Scripture   _____

_____

_____

_____

My Activities Today   Scripture   _____

_____

_____

_____

Special Concern

_____

_____

_____

Missionary

_____

_____

_____

GRACE FOR THE JOURNEY

And God is able to make all grace abound to you, so that in all things at all times, having all that you need, you will abound in every good work.
2 Corinthians 9:8

DAILY PRAYER

Praise and Proclaim, Offer Thanks, Search and Confess,
Listen, Apply Armor

Date _____

Personal Needs   Scripture   _____

_____

_____

_____

_____

Immediate Family   Scripture   _____

_____

_____

_____

My Activities Today   Scripture   _____

_____

_____

_____

Special Concern

_____

_____

_____

Missionary

_____

_____

_____

GRACE FOR THE JOURNEY

This is the confidence we have in approaching God;
that if we ask anything according to his will, he hears us.
1 John 5:14

DAILY PRAYER

Praise and Proclaim, Offer Thanks, Search and Confess,
Listen, Apply Armor

Date _____

Personal Needs   Scripture _____

_____

_____

_____

_____

Immediate Family   Scripture _____

_____

_____

_____

My Activities Today   Scripture _____

_____

_____

_____

Special Concern

_____

_____

_____

Missionary

_____

_____

_____

We have come to share in Christ if we hold firmly
till the end the confidence we had at first.
Hebrews 3:14

DAILY PRAYER

Praise and Proclaim, Offer Thanks, Search and Confess, Listen, Apply Armor

Date _____

Personal Needs   Scripture   _____

_____

_____

_____

_____

Immediate Family   Scripture   _____

_____

_____

_____

My Activities Today   Scripture   _____

_____

_____

_____

Special Concern

_____

_____

_____

Missionary

_____

_____

_____

Blessed is the man who listens to me, watching daily at my doors, waiting at my doorway. For whoever finds me finds life and receives favor from the LORD.
Proverbs 8:34–35

DAILY

DAILY PRAYER

Praise and Proclaim, Offer Thanks, Search and Confess, Listen, Apply Armor

Date _____

Personal Needs   Scripture _____

_____

_____

_____

_____

Immediate Family   Scripture _____

_____

_____

_____

My Activities Today   Scripture _____

_____

_____

_____

Special Concern

_____

_____

_____

Missionary

_____

_____

_____

God's temple is sacred, and you are that temple.
1 Corinthians 3:17b

DAILY PRAYER

Praise and Proclaim, Offer Thanks, Search and Confess,
Listen, Apply Armor

Date _____

DAILY

Personal Needs   Scripture   _____

_____

_____

_____

_____

Immediate Family   Scripture   _____

_____

_____

_____

My Activities Today   Scripture   _____

_____

_____

_____

Special Concern

_____

_____

_____

Missionary

_____

_____

_____

GRACE FOR THE JOURNEY

The LORD is with me; I will not be afraid . . .
The LORD is with me; he is my helper.
Psalm 118:6–7

DAILY PRAYER

Praise and Proclaim, Offer Thanks, Search and Confess,
Listen, Apply Armor

Date _____

Personal Needs   Scripture _____

_____

_____

_____

_____

Immediate Family   Scripture _____

_____

_____

_____

My Activities Today   Scripture _____

_____

_____

_____

Special Concern

_____

_____

_____

Missionary

_____

_____

_____

GRACE FOR THE JOURNEY

May my supplication come before you;
deliver me according to your promise.
Psalm 119:170

DAILY PRAYER

Praise and Proclaim, Offer Thanks, Search and Confess,
Listen, Apply Armor

Date _____

Personal Needs   Scripture _____

_____

_____

_____

_____

Immediate Family   Scripture _____

_____

_____

_____

My Activities Today   Scripture _____

_____

_____

_____

Special Concern

_____

_____

_____

Missionary

_____

_____

_____

And he who searches our hearts knows the mind of the Spirit,
because the Spirit intercedes for the saints in accordance with God's will.
Romans 8:27

DAILY

DAILY PRAYER

Praise and Proclaim, Offer Thanks, Search and Confess,
Listen, Apply Armor

Date _____

Personal Needs   Scripture _____

_____

_____

_____

_____

Immediate Family   Scripture _____

_____

_____

_____

My Activities Today   Scripture _____

_____

_____

_____

Special Concern

_____

_____

_____

Missionary

_____

_____

_____

171

*As for the saints who are in the land, they are the glorious ones in
whom is all my delight.*
Psalm 16:3

DAILY PRAYER

Praise and Proclaim, Offer Thanks, Search and Confess,
Listen, Apply Armor

Date _____

Personal Needs   Scripture _____

_____

_____

_____

_____

Immediate Family   Scripture _____

_____

_____

_____

My Activities Today   Scripture _____

_____

_____

_____

Special Concern

_____

_____

_____

Missionary

_____

_____

_____

GRACE FOR THE JOURNEY

But he said to me, "My grace is sufficient for you, for my power is made perfect in weakness." Therefore I will boast all the more gladly about my weaknesses, so that Christ's power may rest on me.
2 Corinthians 12:9

DAILY PRAYER

Praise and Proclaim, Offer Thanks, Search and Confess,
Listen, Apply Armor

Date _____

Personal Needs   Scripture _____

_____

_____

_____

_____

Immediate Family   Scripture _____

_____

_____

_____

My Activities Today   Scripture _____

_____

_____

_____

Special Concern

_____

_____

_____

Missionary

_____

_____

_____

Therefore he is able to save completely those who come to God through him,
because he always lives to intercede for them.
Hebrews 7:25

Praise and Proclaim, Offer Thanks, Search and Confess,
Listen, Apply Armor

DAILY

Date _____

Personal Needs   Scripture   _____

_____

_____

_____

_____

Immediate Family   Scripture   _____

_____

_____

_____

My Activities Today   Scripture   _____

_____

_____

_____

Special Concern

_____

_____

_____

Missionary

_____

_____

_____

GRACE FOR THE JOURNEY

*Go now, write it on a tablet for them, inscribe it on a scroll,
that for the days to come it may be an everlasting witness.*
Isaiah 30:8

DAILY

DAILY PRAYER

Praise and Proclaim, Offer Thanks, Search and Confess,
Listen, Apply Armor

Date _____

Personal Needs   Scripture   _____

_____

_____

_____

_____

Immediate Family   Scripture   _____

_____

_____

_____

My Activities Today   Scripture   _____

_____

_____

_____

Special Concern

_____

_____

_____

Missionary

_____

_____

_____

Do not fear . . . do not let your hands hang limp.
The LORD your God is with you, he is mighty to save.
He will take great delight in you, he will quiet you with his love,
he will rejoice over you with singing.
Zephaniah 3:16–17

DAILY PRAYER

Praise and Proclaim, Offer Thanks, Search and Confess, Listen, Apply Armor

Date _____

Personal Needs   Scripture   _____

_____

_____

_____

_____

Immediate Family   Scripture   _____

_____

_____

_____

My Activities Today   Scripture   _____

_____

_____

_____

Special Concern

_____

_____

_____

Missionary

_____

_____

_____

181

Give ear and come to me; hear me, that your soul may live,
I will make an everlasting covenant with you,
my faithful love promised to David.
Isaiah 55:3

DAILY

DAILY PRAYER

Praise and Proclaim, Offer Thanks, Search and Confess,
Listen, Apply Armor

Date _____

Personal Needs   Scripture _____

_____

_____

_____

_____

Immediate Family   Scripture _____

_____

_____

_____

My Activities Today   Scripture _____

_____

_____

_____

Special Concern

_____

_____

_____

Missionary

_____

_____

_____

*How awesome is this place! This is none other than
the house of God; this is the gate of heaven.*
Genesis 28:17

DAILY

DAILY PRAYER

Praise and Proclaim, Offer Thanks, Search and Confess,
Listen, Apply Armor

Date _____

Personal Needs   Scripture _____

_____

_____

_____

_____

Immediate Family   Scripture _____

_____

_____

_____

My Activities Today   Scripture _____

_____

_____

_____

Special Concern

_____

_____

_____

Missionary

_____

_____

_____

LORD, you have been our dwelling place throughout all generations.
Before the mountains were born and you brought forth the earth.
. . . from everlasting to everlasting you are God.
Psalm 90:1–2

DAILY PRAYER

Praise and Proclaim, Offer Thanks, Search and Confess,
Listen, Apply Armor

Date _____

Personal Needs   Scripture   _____

_____

_____

_____

_____

Immediate Family   Scripture   _____

_____

_____

_____

My Activities Today   Scripture   _____

_____

_____

_____

Special Concern

_____

_____

_____

Missionary

_____

_____

_____

GRACE FOR THE JOURNEY

Be joyful always; pray continually; give thanks in all circumstances,
for this is God's will for you in Christ Jesus.
1 Thessalonians 5:16

DAILY

DAILY PRAYER

Praise and Proclaim, Offer Thanks, Search and Confess,
Listen, Apply Armor

Date _____

Personal Needs   Scripture   _____

_____

_____

_____

_____

Immediate Family   Scripture   _____

_____

_____

_____

My Activities Today   Scripture   _____

_____

_____

_____

Special Concern

_____

_____

_____

Missionary

_____

_____

_____

My dear children, I write this to you so that you will not sin.
But if anybody does sin, we have one who speaks to the Father
in our defense—Jesus Christ, the Righteous One.
1 John 2:1

DAILY

_____

_____

_____

_____

_____

_____

_____

_____

_____

_____

_____

_____

_____

_____

_____

_____

_____

_____

_____

_____

_____

_____

_____

DAILY PRAYER

Praise and Proclaim, Offer Thanks, Search and Confess,
Listen, Apply Armor

DAILY

Date _____

Personal Needs   Scripture _____

_____

_____

_____

_____

Immediate Family   Scripture _____

_____

_____

_____

My Activities Today   Scripture _____

_____

_____

_____

Special Concern

_____

_____

_____

Missionary

_____

_____

_____

Those who cling to worthless idols forfeit the grace that could be theirs.
Jonah 2:8

DAILY

DAILY PRAYER

Praise and Proclaim, Offer Thanks, Search and Confess,
Listen, Apply Armor

Date _____

Personal Needs   Scripture   _____

_____

_____

_____

_____

Immediate Family   Scripture   _____

_____

_____

_____

My Activities Today   Scripture   _____

_____

_____

_____

Special Concern

_____

_____

_____

Missionary

_____

_____

_____

GRACE FOR THE JOURNEY

Let us then approach the throne of grace with confidence, so that we may receive mercy and find grace to help us in our time of need.
Hebrews 4:16

DAILY

DAILY PRAYER

Praise and Proclaim, Offer Thanks, Search and Confess,
Listen, Apply Armor

Date _____

DAILY

Personal Needs   Scripture   _____

_____

_____

_____

_____

Immediate Family   Scripture   _____

_____

_____

_____

My Activities Today   Scripture   _____

_____

_____

_____

Special Concern

_____

_____

_____

Missionary

_____

_____

_____

For he bore the sins of many and made intercession for the transgressors.
Isaiah 53:12b

DAILY

_____

_____

_____

_____

_____

_____

_____

_____

_____

_____

_____

_____

_____

_____

_____

_____

_____

_____

_____

_____

DAILY PRAYER

Praise and Proclaim, Offer Thanks, Search and Confess,
Listen, Apply Armor

Date _____

Personal Needs   Scripture   _____

_____

_____

_____

_____

Immediate Family   Scripture   _____

_____

_____

_____

My Activities Today   Scripture   _____

_____

_____

_____

Special Concern

_____

_____

_____

Missionary

_____

_____

_____

I consider my life worth nothing to me, if only I may finish the race and complete the task the Lord Jesus has given me—the task of testifying to the gospel of God's grace.
Acts 20:24

DAILY

_____

DAILY PRAYER

Praise and Proclaim, Offer Thanks, Search and Confess,
Listen, Apply Armor

Date _____

Personal Needs   Scripture   _____

_____

_____

_____

_____

Immediate Family   Scripture   _____

_____

_____

_____

My Activities Today   Scripture   _____

_____

_____

_____

Special Concern

_____

_____

_____

Missionary

_____

_____

_____

199

*The four living creatures and twenty-four elders fell down before
the Lamb. Each one had a harp and they were holding golden
bowls full of incense, which are the prayers of the saints.*
Revelation 5:8

WEEKDAY PRAYER
PAGES

Sunday

Intercessory Prayer Guide

Prayers for the Church

In *The Invitation*, see chapter, God's Kingdom Come—Prayer for the Church.

LORD, you said if we, your people, who are called by your name, will humble ourselves and pray and seek your face and turn from our wicked ways, then you will hear from heaven and will forgive our sin and will heal our land. (2 Chr 7:14)

LORD, we pray that we may know you, the only true God, and Jesus Christ, whom you have sent. Holy Father, protect us by the power of your name—the name you have given Jesus—so that we may be one as you are one. Sanctify us by the truth; your word is truth . . . May we be brought to complete unity to let the world know that you sent Jesus and have loved us even as you have loved him. (Jn 17:3, 11, 17, 23b)

LORD, give us grace to love one another as you have loved us, so we must love one another. By this all men will know that we are your disciples, if we love one another. (Jn 13:35)

As God's fellow workers we pray and urge you not to receive God's grace in vain. For he says, "In the time of my favor I heard you, and in the day of salvation I helped you." I tell you, now is the time of God's favor, now is the day of salvation. May we put no stumbling block in anyone's path, so that our ministry will not be discredited. May you open wide our hearts to you, to restore, to reassign, . . . to say to the captive, "Come out" and to those in darkness, "Be free!" (2 Cor 6:1–3, 13, Is 49:8–9)

Let us consider how we may spur one another on toward love and good deeds. Let us not give up meeting together, as some are in the habit of doing, but let us encourage on another—and all the more as you see the Day approaching. (Heb 10:24–25)

Church Leadership—Pastors, Staff, Elders, and Families

LORD, I pray that out of your glorious riches you may strengthen _____ with power through your Spirit in his/her inner being. (Eph 3:16)

LORD, give grace to _____ that whenever they open their mouth, words may be given so that he/she will fearlessly make known the mystery of the gospel. (Eph 6:19)

Father, may _____ 's love abound more and more in knowledge and depth of insight, so that he/she may be able to discern what is best and may be pure and blameless until the day of Christ, filled with the fruit of righteousness that comes through Jesus Christ—to the glory and praise of God. (Phil 1:9–11)

LORD, if we have any encouragement from being united with Christ, if any comfort from his love, if any fellowship with the Spirit, if any tenderness and compassion, then make our joy complete by being like-minded, having the same love, being one in spirit and purpose. Help us do nothing out of selfish ambition or vain conceit, but in humility consider others better than ourselves. Help each of us not only look to our own interests, but also to the interests of others. May our attitude be the same as that of Christ Jesus. (Phil 2:1–5)

LORD, we have not stopped praying for _____ asking you to fill _____ with the knowledge of your will through all spiritual wisdom and understanding. And we pray this in order that they may live a life worthy of the Lord. May he/she please you in every way: bearing fruit in every good work, growing in the knowledge of God, being strengthened with all power according to his glorious might so that _____ may have great endurance, patience, and joyfully giving thanks. (Col 1:9–12a)

LORD, help our leaders be shepherds of God's flock that is under their care, serving as overseers—not because they must, but because they are willing, as God wants them to be; not greedy for money, but eager to serve; not lording it over those entrusted to them, but being examples to the flock. And when the Chief Shepherd appears, they will receive the crown of glory that will never fade away . . . I pray they clothe themselves with humility toward one another. (1 Pt 5:2–5)

SUNDAY

Sunday

Intercessory Prayer Guide

Church Ministries

May he turn our hearts to him, to walk in all his ways, to keep his commands . . . And may these words of mine which I have prayed before the LORD—be near to the LORD our God day and night, that he may uphold the cause of his servant . . . according to each days need. (1 Kgs 8:58–59)

May _____ continue to work out his/her salvation with fear and trembling, for it is God who works in him/her to will and to act according to his good purpose. May _____ do everything without complaining or arguing, so that he/she may become blameless and pure, a child of God without fault in a crooked and depraved generation, in which he shines like stars in the universe as he/she holds out the word of life—in order that he/she may boast on the day of Christ that _____ did not run or labor for nothing. (Phil 2:12–16)

May the LORD make our love increase and overflow for each other and for everyone else, . . . May he strengthen our hearts so that you will be blameless and holy in the presence of our God and Father when our Lord Jesus comes with all his holy ones. (1 Thes 3:12–13)

LORD, your divine power has given us everything we need for life and godliness through our knowledge of you who called us by your own glory and goodness. Through these you have given us your very great and precious promises, so that through them we may participate in the divine nature and escape the corruption in the world caused by evil desires. For this very reason, we make every effort to add to our faith goodness; and to goodness, knowledge; and to knowledge, self-control; and to self-control, perseverance; and to perseverance, godliness; and to godliness, brotherly kindness; and to brotherly kindness, love. For if we possess these qualities in increasing measure, they will keep us from being ineffective and unproductive in our knowledge of our Lord Jesus Christ. (2 Pt 1:2–8)

Sunday

Intercessory Prayer Guide

Lost and Unrepentant

I will search for the lost and bring back the strays. I will bind up the injured and strengthen the weak. (Ez 34:16a)

Surely the arm of the LORD is not too short to save, nor his ear too dull to hear. (Is 59:1)

Father, help me to pray and seek to pursue _____ in the same way you, Father in heaven are not willing that any of these little ones should be lost. (Mt 18:14)

Suppose one of you has a hundred sheep and loses one of them. Does he not leave the ninety-nine in the open country and go after the lost sheep until he finds it? LORD, show me how to seek after the lost sheep. (Lk 15:4)

I pray for _____ to repent and turn back to you because there is rejoicing in the presence of the angels of God over one sinner who repents. (Lk 15:10)

For the Son of Man came to seek and to save what was lost. How much, O LORD, we long for _____ to be saved by you. (Lk 19:10)

This happened so that the words he had spoken would be fulfilled: "I have not lost one of those you gave me." (Jn 18:9)

I am astonished that you are so quickly deserting the one who called you by the grace of Christ and are turning to a different gospel— (Gal 1:6)

You who are trying to be justified by law have been alienated from Christ; you have fallen away from grace. (Gal 5:4)

He has lost connection with the Head, from whom the whole body, supported and held together by its ligaments and sinews, grows as God causes it to grow. (Col 2:19)

In your unfailing love you will lead the people you have redeemed.
In your strength you will guide them to your holy dwelling.
Exodus 15:13

Sunday

Date _____

The Church

_____
_____
_____

Church Leadership—Pastors, Staff, Elders, and Families

_____
_____
_____

Church Ministries

_____
_____
_____

Lost and Unrepentant

_____
_____
_____

SUNDAY

For in the day of trouble, he will keep me safe in his dwelling;
he will hide me in the shelter of his tabernacle
and set me high upon a rock.
Psalm 27:5

Sunday

Date _____

The Church

_____

_____

_____

Church Leadership—Pastors, Staff, Elders, and Families

_____

_____

_____

Church Ministries

_____

_____

_____

Lost and Unrepentant

_____

_____

_____

SUNDAY

Therefore I tell you, whatever you ask for in prayer,
believe that you have received it, and it will be yours.
Mark 11:24

Sunday

Date _____

The Church

_____

_____

_____

Church Leadership—Pastors, Staff, Elders, and Families

_____

_____

_____

Church Ministries

_____

_____

_____

Lost and Unrepentant

_____

_____

_____

SUNDAY

Come and see what God has done, how awesome his works in man's behalf!
Psalm 66:5

Sunday

Date _____

The Church

_____

_____

_____

Church Leadership—Pastors, Staff, Elders, and Families

_____

_____

_____

Church Ministries

_____

_____

_____

Lost and Unrepentant

_____

_____

_____

SUNDAY

And I will do whatever you ask in my name,
so that the Son may bring glory to the Father.
John 14:13

Sunday

Date _____

The Church

_____

_____

_____

Church Leadership—Pastors, Staff, Elders, and Families

_____

_____

_____

Church Ministries

_____

_____

_____

Lost and Unrepentant

_____

_____

_____

For by the grace given me I say to every one of you: Do not think of yourself more highly than you ought, but rather think of yourself with sober judgment, in accordance with the measure of faith God has given you.
Romans 12:3

Sunday

Date ———————

The Church

_____

_____

_____

Church Leadership—Pastors, Staff, Elders, and Families

_____

_____

_____

Church Ministries

_____

_____

_____

Lost and Unrepentant

_____

_____

_____

Devote yourselves to prayer, being watchful and thankful.
Colossians 4:2

Sunday

Date _____

The Church

_____

_____

_____

Church Leadership—Pastors, Staff, Elders, and Families

_____

_____

_____

Church Ministries

_____

_____

_____

Lost and Unrepentant

_____

_____

_____

Then Jesus told his disciples a parable to show them that they should
always pray and not give up.
Luke 18:1

Sunday

Date _____

SUNDAY

The Church

_____

_____

_____

Church Leadership—Pastors, Staff, Elders, and Families

_____

_____

_____

Church Ministries

_____

_____

_____

Lost and Unrepentant

_____

_____

_____

Very early in the morning, while it was still dark, Jesus got up, left the house and went off to a solitary place, where he prayed.
Mark 1:35

Sunday

Date _____

The Church

_____

_____

_____

Church Leadership—Pastors, Staff, Elders, and Families

_____

_____

_____

Church Ministries

_____

_____

_____

Lost and Unrepentant

_____

_____

_____

Your dwelling place is secure, your nest is set in a rock.
Numbers 24:21a

Sunday

Date _____

The Church

_____

_____

_____

Church Leadership—Pastors, Staff, Elders, and Families

_____

_____

_____

Church Ministries

_____

_____

_____

Lost and Unrepentant

_____

_____

_____

SUNDAY

Hear from heaven, your dwelling place. Forgive and act;
deal with each man according to all he does, since you know
his heart (for you alone know the hearts of all men).
1 Kings 8:39

Sunday

Date _____

The Church

_____

_____

_____

Church Leadership—Pastors, Staff, Elders, and Families

_____

_____

_____

Church Ministries

_____

_____

_____

Lost and Unrepentant

_____

_____

_____

SUNDAY

Monday

Intercessory Prayer Guide

Missionaries

LORD, thank you for how beautiful on the mountains are the feet of those who bring good news, who proclaim peace, who bring good tidings, who proclaim salvation, who say to Zion, "Your God reigns." (Is 52:7)

You are _____'s hiding place; you will protect him/her from trouble and surround her with songs of deliverance. (Ps 32:7)

Dear Jesus, you said, "All authority in heaven and on earth has been given to us. Therefore, _____, has obeyed and gone to make disciples of all nations; baptizing them in the name of the Father and of the Son and of the Holy Spirit, and teaching them to obey everything you have commanded us. And surely you are with them always, to the very end of the age." (Mt 28:18–20)

We eagerly expect and hope that _____ will in no way be ashamed, but will have sufficient courage so that now as always Christ will be exalted in his body whether by life or by death. (Phil 1:20)

We always thank God for _____, mentioning them in our prayers. We continually remember before our God and Father their work produced by faith, their labor prompted by love, and their endurance inspired by hope in our Lord Jesus Christ. (1 Thes 1:2–3)

Missionaries

For we know, brothers loved by God, that he has chosen you, because the gospel came to you not simply with words, but also with power, with the Holy Spirit and with deep conviction . . . you became imitators of the LORD; in spite of severe suffering, you welcomed the message with the joy given by the Holy Spirit. And so you became a model to all the believers in (city). May the Lord's message ring out from _____ not only in (city) and (country)—their faith in God has become known everywhere . . . May you use them to turn many to God from idols to serve the living and true God. (1 Thes 1:4–9)

Finally, brothers, we pray for _____ —that the message of the Lord may spread rapidly and be honored. And we pray that _____ may be delivered from wicked and evil men, for not everyone has faith. But the Lord is faithful, and he will strengthen and protect them from the evil one. May the Lord direct _____ heart into God's love and Christ's perseverance. (2 Thes 3:1–3, 5)

Lord, we pray for _____ that God may open a door for your Word, so that he/she may proclaim the mystery of Christ. (Col 4:3)

MONDAY

Monday

Intercessory Prayer Guide

Your Ministry

Pray for good stewardship of time, talents, and money; assistance, vision, purpose, discovery, and development of spiritual gifts, insight into God's will, leading and shepherding of His flock.

Unless the LORD builds the house, its builders labor in vain. Unless the LORD watches over the city, the watchmen stand guard in vain. Protect us from laboring in vain. We need your discernment and strength in establishing and sustaining this ministry. (Ps 127:1)

Let the peace of Christ rule in our hearts, since as members of one body we were called to peace. And be thankful. Let the word of Christ dwell in us richly as we teach and admonish one another with all wisdom, and as we sing psalms, hymns and spiritual songs with gratitude in our hearts to God. And whatever we do, whether in word or deed, do it all in the name of the Lord Jesus, giving thanks to God the Father through him. (Col 3:15–17)

LORD, you said, if any of you lacks wisdom, he should ask God, who gives generously to all without finding fault, and it will be given to him. Please give _____ wisdom. (Jas 1:5)

Heavenly Father, for attaining wisdom and discipline; for understanding words of insight; for acquiring a disciplined and prudent life, doing what is right and just and fair; for giving prudence to the simple, knowledge and discretion to the young—let the wise listen and add to their learning, and let the discerning get guidance—for the fear of the LORD is the beginning of knowledge. (Prv 1:1–7)

Poor and Hungry

Thank you, LORD, you defend the cause of the weak and fatherless; maintain the rights of the poor and oppressed. (Ps 82:3)

Thank you, LORD, for you satisfy the thirsty and fill the hungry with good things. (Ps 107:9)

Use us, LORD, to scattered abroad gifts to the poor. (Ps 112:9)

Open your hand and satisfy the desires of every living thing. LORD uphold the cause of the oppressed and give food to the hungry. (Ps 145:16, Ps 146:7)

LORD, you say, "He who is kind to the poor lends to you and you will reward him for what he has done. Show us how to open our arms to the poor and extend our hands to the needy." (Prv 19:17, 31:20)

Help us remember that we are equal in your sight that the rich and poor have this in common: the LORD is the Maker of us all. May we be generous and receive blessing, as we share food with the poor. (Prv 22:2, 9)

If we spend ourselves in behalf of the hungry and satisfy the needs of the oppressed, then your light will rise in the darkness, and your night will become like noonday. (Is 58:10)

MONDAY

*You will go out with joy and be led forth in peace; the
mountains and the hills will burst into song before you,
and all the trees of the field will clap their hands.*
Isaiah 55:12

Monday

Date _____

Missionaries

_____

_____

_____

Your Ministry

_____

_____

Poor and Hungry

_____

_____

Come and listen, all you who fear God;
let me tell you what he has done for me.
Psalm 66:16

Monday

Date _____

Missionaries

_____

_____

_____

Your Ministry

_____

_____

_____

Poor and Hungry

_____

_____

_____

MONDAY

I call to you, O LORD, every day; I spread out my hands to you . . .
in the morning my prayer comes before you.
Psalm 88:9b, 13b

Monday

Date _____

Missionaries

_____

_____

_____

Your Ministry

_____

_____

_____

Poor and Hungry

_____

_____

_____

MONDAY

With honey from a rock I will satisfy you.
Psalm 81:16b

Monday

Date _____

Missionaries

_____

_____

_____

Your Ministry

_____

_____

_____

Poor and Hungry

_____

_____

_____

MONDAY

Blessed are those whose strength is in you,
who have set their hearts on a pilgrimage.
Psalm 84:5

Monday

Date _____

Missionaries

_____

_____

_____

Your Ministry

_____

_____

_____

Poor and Hungry

_____

_____

_____

MONDAY

How lovely is your dwelling place, O LORD Almighty!
Psalm 84:1

Monday

Date _____

Missionaries

_____

_____

_____

Your Ministry

_____

_____

_____

Poor and Hungry

_____

_____

_____

MONDAY

Light is shed upon the righteous and joy on the upright in heart.
Psalm 97:11

Monday

Date _____

Missionaries

_____

_____

_____

Your Ministry

_____

_____

_____

Poor and Hungry

_____

_____

_____

MONDAY

Great are the works of the LORD; they are pondered
by all who delight in them.
Psalm 111:2

Monday

Date _____

Missionaries

_____

_____

_____

Your Ministry

_____

_____

_____

Poor and Hungry

_____

_____

_____

MONDAY

My soul finds rest in God alone; my hope comes from him.
Psalm 62:5

Monday

Date _____

Missionaries

_____

_____

_____

Your Ministry

_____

_____

_____

Poor and Hungry

_____

_____

_____

MONDAY

For whoever finds me finds life and receives favor from the LORD.
Proverbs 8:35

Monday

Date _____

Missionaries

_____
_____
_____

Your Ministry

_____
_____
_____

Poor and Hungry

_____
_____
_____

MONDAY

*But just as you excel in everything—in faith, in speech, in knowledge,
in complete earnestness and in your love for us—see that
you also excel in this grace of giving.*
2 Corinthians 8:7

Monday

Date _____

Missionaries

_____

_____

_____

Your Ministry

_____

_____

Poor and Hungry

_____

_____

_____

Tuesday

Intercessory Prayer Guide

Thank God for His Promises

The LORD himself goes before you and will be with you; he will never leave you nor forsake you. Do not be afraid; do not be discouraged. (Dt 31:8)

Thank you, LORD, that the beloved of the LORD rest secure in you, for you shield me all day long, and the one the LORD loves rests between his shoulders. (Dt 33:12)

Thank you, Father, for you will keep in perfect peace him whose mind is steadfast, because he trusts in you. (Is 26:3)

So do not fear, for I am with you; do not be dismayed, for I am your God. I will strengthen you and help you; I will uphold you with my righteous right hand. (Is 41:10)

Thank you, LORD, for asking us to come to you, all you who are weary and burdened, and you will give us rest. (Mt 11:28)

LORD, we thank you, with you God, all things are possible. (Mt 19:26)

Thank you, LORD, that you have not left us abandoned. God has come to help his people. (Lk 7:16)

However, as it is written: "No eye has seen, no ear has heard, no mind has conceived what God has prepared for those who love him." (1 Cor 2:9)

God who supplies seed to the sower and bread for food will also supply and increase our store of seed and will enlarge the harvest of our righteousness. (1 Cor 9:10)

Thank you, LORD for promising to meet all our needs according to your glorious riches in Christ Jesus. (Phil 4:19)

Thank you, LORD with you is full redemption, the forgiveness of sins. (Ps 130:7, Col 1:14)

TUESDAY

Tuesday

Intercessory Prayer Guide

Teens/Youth

Dear Father, may _____'s delight be in the law of the LORD, and on his law he meditates day and night. May _____ be like a tree planted by streams of water, which yields its fruit in season and whose leaf does not wither. Whatever he does prospers. (Ps 1:2–3)

How can a young man keep his way pure? By living according to your word. May _____ seek you with all his/her heart; do not let them stray from your commands. May your word be hidden in their heart that _____ might not sin against you. Open _____'s eyes that he may see wonderful things in your law. (Ps 119:9–11, 18)

Direct _____ in the path of your commands, for there he finds delight. Turn his/her heart toward your statutes and not toward selfish gain. Turn his/her eyes away from worthless things; preserve _____'s life according to your word. May he/she seek your face with all his/her heart; be gracious to _____ according to your promise. (Ps 119:35–37, 58)

LORD, you promise that no temptation has seized _____ except what is common to man. And God, you are faithful; you will not let _____ be tempted beyond what he can bear. But when he is tempted, you will also provide a way out so that he can stand up under it. (1 Cor 10:13)

May _____ flee the evil desires of youth, and pursue righteousness, faith, love, and peace, along with those who call on the LORD out of a pure heart. . . . May he/she avoid foolish arguments and be kind to everyone. Help us gently instruct when we oppose in view of your truth, in the hope that you, God, will grant them repentance leading them to a knowledge of the truth, and that they will come to their senses and escape from the trap of the devil, who has taken them captive to do his will. (1 Tm 2:22–26)

Tuesday

Intercessory Prayer Guide

Trials and Troubles of Your Heart

The righteous cry out, and the LORD hears them; he delivers them from all their troubles. The LORD is close to the brokenhearted and saves those who are crushed in spirit. (Ps 34:17–18)

The LORD is with me; I will not be afraid. What can man do to me? The LORD is with me; he is my helper. I will look in triumph on my enemies. It is better to take refuge in the LORD than to trust in man. (Ps 118:6–8)

May I trust in you with all my heart and lean not on my own understanding; in all my ways acknowledge you, and you will make my paths straight. (Prv 3:5–6)

Praise be to the God and Father of our Lord Jesus Christ, the Father of compassion and the God of all comfort, who comforts us in all our troubles, so that we can comfort those in any trouble with the comfort we ourselves have received from God. (2 Cor 1:3–4)

I consider that our present sufferings are not worth comparing with the glory that will be revealed in us. (Rom 8:18)

In the same way, the Spirit helps us in our weakness. We do not know what we ought to pray for, but the Spirit himself intercedes for us with groans that words cannot express. And we know that in all things God works for the good of those who love him and have been called according to his purpose. (Rom 8:26, 28)

If God is for us, who can be against us? He who did not spare his own Son, but gave him up for us all—how will he not also, along with him, graciously give us all things? Who will bring any charge against those whom God has chosen? It is God who justifies. Who is he that condemns? (Rom 8:31b–34a)

TUESDAY

Trials and Troubles of Your Heart

Christ Jesus, who died—more than that, who was raised to life—is at the right hand of God and is also interceding for us. Who shall separate us from the love of Christ? Shall trouble or hardship or persecution or famine or nakedness or danger or sword? No, in all these things we are more than conquerors through him who loved us. For I am convinced that neither death nor life, neither angels nor demons, neither the present nor the future, nor any powers, neither height nor depth, nor anything else in all creation, will be able to separate us from the love of God that is in Christ Jesus our Lord. (Rom 8:34–35, 37–39)

LORD, help me be satisfied in my present circumstances for you said, "I will not in any way fail you nor give you up nor leave you without support. I will not, I will not, I will not leave you helpless nor forsake you, nor let you down (or relax my hold on you). Assuredly not!" (Heb 13:5 AMP)

. . . Come to my aid. Great is the LORD who delights in blessing his servants with peace. (Ps 35:2 NLT)

LORD, I will not be afraid; I will only believe. (Mk 5:36)

Thank you, Jesus, you promised you will not leave us as orphans (comfortless, desolate, bereaving, forlorn, helpless). You will come. (Jn 14:18 AMP)

We will put our hope in the LORD! He is our help and our shield. In him our hearts rejoice, for we trust in his holy name. Let your unfailing love surround us. LORD, our hope is in you alone. (Ps 33:20–22)

Help me not worry about my life . . . is life not more important than food and clothes? As I look at the birds . . . you, my heavenly father feed them. Am I not much more valuable than they? How can I by worrying add a single hour to my life? (Mt 6:25–27)

If anyone acknowledges that Jesus is the Son of God, God lives in him and he in God. And so we know and rely on the love God has for us. God is love. Whoever lives in love lives in God, and God in him. In this way, love is made complete among us . . . There is no fear in love. But perfect love drives out fear. (1 Jn 4:15–18)

TUESDAY

Tuesday

Intercessory Prayer Guide

Authorities/Leaders	*Pray for by name* (www.usa.gov)
	if possible

1. President _____

2. Vice President _____

3. Supreme Court Justice _____

4. U.S. Senators _____

5. U.S. Congressmen _____

6. Governor _____

7. State Representatives _____

8. County Commissioner _____

9. City Councilmen _____

10. Local Judge _____

11. School Board
    Superintendent _____

12. School Board Members _____

13. School Principals _____

14. Local School Teachers _____

15. Local Universities _____

16. Military _____

17. Local Law Enforcement _____

TUESDAY

Authorities/Leaders

So give your servant a discerning heart to govern your people and to distinguish between right and wrong. For who is able to govern this great people of yours? (1 Kgs 3:9)

May the LORD our God be with us as he was our fathers; may he never leave us or forsake us. May he turn our hearts to him, to walk in all his ways and to keep his commands. (1 Kgs 8:57–58)

Everyone must submit himself to the governing authorities, for there is no authority except that which God has established. The authorities that exist have been established by God. (Rom 13:1)

For by him all things were created: things in heaven and on earth, visible and invisible, whether thrones or powers or rulers or authorities; all things were created by him and for him. (Col 1:16)

We know that the law is good if one uses it properly. (1 Tm 1:8)

I urge you, then, first of all, that requests, prayers, intercession and thanksgiving be made for everyone—for kings and all those in authority, that we may live peaceful and quiet lives in all godliness and holiness. This is good, and pleases God our Savior. (1 Tm 2:1–3)

Restore us again, O God our Savior, and put away your displeasure toward us. Will you be angry with us forever? . . . Revive us again. Surely your salvation is near . . . that your glory may dwell in our land. (Ps 85:3–4, 5a, 6a, 9 NLT)

God, help our country love justice as you do and act justly, love mercy, and walk humbly with you. (Ps 11:7, Mic 6:8)

Father, grant us the conviction to show proper respect toward everyone, as your Word commands. (1 Pet 2:17)

May integrity and honesty be their virtue and their protection because their hope is in you. (Ps 25:21)

TUESDAY

I lift up my eyes to the hills—where does my help come from? My help comes from the LORD the maker of heaven and earth.
Psalm 121:1–2

Tuesday

Date _____

Thank God for His Promises

_____

_____

_____

Teens/Youth

_____

_____

_____

Trials and Troubles of Your Heart

_____

_____

_____

Authorities/Leaders

_____

_____

_____

TUESDAY

God has set you above your companions by anointing you with the oil of joy.
Psalm 45:7b

Tuesday

Date ———————

Thank God for His Promises

_____
_____
_____

Teens/Youth

_____
_____
_____

Trials and Troubles of Your Heart

_____
_____
_____

Authorities/Leaders

_____
_____
_____

TUESDAY

You will be a crown of splendor in the LORD's hand,
a royal diadem in the hand of God.
Isaiah 62:3

Tuesday

Date _____

Thank God for His Promises

_____

_____

_____

Teens/Youth

_____

_____

_____

Trials and Troubles of Your Heart

_____

_____

_____

Authorities/Leaders

_____

_____

_____

TUESDAY

Why are you downcast O my soul? Why so disturbed within me?
Put your hope in God.
Psalm 42:5

Tuesday

Date _____

Thank God for His Promises

_____

_____

_____

Teens/Youth

_____

_____

_____

Trials and Troubles of Your Heart

_____

_____

_____

Authorities/Leaders

_____

_____

_____

I am the LORD who heals you.
Exodus 15:26b

Tuesday

Date _____

Thank God for His Promises

_____

_____

_____

Teens/Youth

_____

_____

_____

Trials and Troubles of Your Heart

_____

_____

_____

Authorities/Leaders

_____

_____

_____

TUESDAY

The law of the LORD is perfect, reviving the soul.
Psalm 19:7

Tuesday

Date _____

Thank God for His Promises

_____

_____

_____

Teens/Youth

_____

_____

_____

Trials and Troubles of Your Heart

_____

_____

_____

Authorities/Leaders

_____

_____

_____

TUESDAY

*I am the LORD your God, who teaches you what is best for you,
who directs you in the way you should go.*
Isaiah 48:17b

Tuesday

Date _____

Thank God for His Promises

_____

_____

_____

Teens/Youth

_____

_____

_____

Trials and Troubles of Your Heart

_____

_____

_____

Authorities/Leaders

_____

_____

_____

TUESDAY

Trust in him at all times, O people; pour out your hearts to him.
Psalm 62:8

Tuesday

Date _____

Thank God for His Promises

_____

_____

_____

Teens/Youth

_____

_____

_____

Trials and Troubles of Your Heart

_____

_____

_____

Authorities/Leaders

_____

_____

_____

Of the increase of his government and peace there will be no end. He will reign on David's throne and over his kingdom, establishing and upholding it with justice and righteousness from that time on and forever.
Isaiah 9:7

Tuesday

Date _____

Thank God for His Promises

_____
_____
_____

Teens/Youth

_____
_____
_____

Trials and Troubles of Your Heart

_____
_____
_____

Authorities/Leaders

_____
_____
_____

*Those who look to him are radiant; their faces are
never covered with shame.*
Psalm 34:5

Tuesday

Date _____

Thank God for His Promises

_____

_____

_____

Teens/Youth

_____

_____

_____

Trials and Troubles of Your Heart

_____

_____

_____

Authorities/Leaders

_____

_____

_____

For the law was given through Moses;
grace and truth came through Jesus Christ.
John 1:17

Tuesday

Date _____

Thank God for His Promises

_____

_____

_____

Teens/Youth

_____

_____

_____

Trials and Troubles of Your Heart

_____

_____

_____

Authorities/Leaders

_____

_____

_____

TUESDAY

Wednesday

Intercessory Prayer Guide

Waiting on the LORD

The LORD will fight for you; you need only be still. (Ex 14:14)

Now then, stand still and see this great thing the LORD is about to do before your eyes. (1 Sm 12:16)

Wait for the LORD; be strong and take heart and wait for the LORD. (Ps 27:14)

Help me, Father to be still, and know that you are God, the great I AM. (Ps 46:10a)

From Zion, perfect in beauty, God shines forth. Our God comes and will not be silent. (Ps 50:2)

I wait for the LORD, my soul waits, and in his word I put my hope. (Ps 130:5)

Dear LORD, I have stilled and quieted my soul like a weaned child. (Ps 131:2)

Thank you, LORD, for your grace to me; that you rise to show me compassion. For you are a God of justice. I am blessed when I wait for you! (Is 30:18)

The LORD is good to those whose hope is in him, to the one who seeks him; it is good to wait quietly for the salvation of the LORD. (Lam 3:25–26)

For the grace of God has appeared to all men. It teach us to say "No" to ungodliness and worldly passions, and to live self-controlled, upright and godly lives in this present age, while we wait for the blessed hope—the glorious appearing of our great God and Savior, Jesus Christ. (Ti 2:11–13)

Help us to wait for your Son from heaven, whom you raised from the dead—Jesus, who rescues us. (1 Thes 1:10)

Wednesday

Intercessory Prayer Guide

Worship

You may want to sing worship songs or hymns during this time. It may be helpful to purchase a small song book or book of hymns.

I will ascribe to the LORD the glory due his name. I will bring an offering and come before him; I will worship the LORD in the splendor of his holiness. (1 Chr 16:29)

Clap your hands, all you nations; shout to God with cries of joy. (Ps 47:1)

I will praise God's name in song and glorify Him with thanksgiving. This will please the LORD more than an ox. (Ps 69:30)

Come, let us sing for joy to the LORD; let us shout aloud to the Rock of our salvation. (Ps 95:1)

Come, let us bow down in worship, let us kneel before the LORD our Maker. (Ps 95:6)

Praise God in his sanctuary; praise him in his mighty heavens. Praise him for his acts of power; praise him for his surpassing greatness. Praise him with the sounding of the trumpet, praise him with the harp and lyre, praise him with tambourine and dancing. (Ps 150:1–4)

God is spirit, and his worshipers must worship in spirit and in truth. (Jn 4:24)

In view of your mercy God, I offer my body as a living sacrifice, holy and pleasing to you—this is my spiritual act of worship. (Rom 12:1)

Sing and make music in your heart to the LORD. (Eph 5:19b)

Sing psalms, hymns and spiritual songs with gratitude in your hearts to God. (Col 3:16b)

I want men everywhere to lift up holy hands in prayer. (1 Tm 2:8)

WEDNESDAY

Wednesday

Intercessory Prayer Guide

Prayers for the Wounded and Sick

The eternal God is your refuge, and underneath are the everlasting arms. (Dt 33:27)

The righteous cry out, and the LORD hears them; he delivers them from all their troubles. The LORD is close to the brokenhearted and saves those who are crushed in spirit. (Ps 34:17–18)

God is our refuge and strength, an ever-present help in trouble. (Ps 46:1)

Wounds from a friend can be trusted, but an enemy multiplies kisses. (Prv 27:6)

Our wounds fester and are loathsome because of our sinful folly. Protect _____ from willful sins. (Ps 38:5)

Thank you for sending forth your word and healing _____. (Ps 107:20)

Thank you, LORD, you promise to heal _____ who is brokenhearted and bind up their wounds. (Ps 147:3)

Blows and wounds cleanse away evil, and beatings purge the inmost being. (Prv 20:30)

Help us remember LORD, Jesus was pierced for our transgressions, he was crushed for our iniquities; the punishment that brought us peace was upon him, and by his wounds we are healed. (Is 53:5)

God, you say you will restore _____ to health and heal his/ her wounds. (Jer 30:17)

Give us humility to confess our sins to each other and pray for each other so that we may be healed. (Jas 5:16)

Wednesday

Intercessory Prayer Guide

Peace in Jerusalem

Save your people and bless your inheritance; be their shepherd and carry them forever. (Ps 28:9)

LORD, we pray for the peace of Jerusalem: may those who love you be secure. How good and pleasant it is when brothers live together in unity! (Ps 122:6, Ps 133:1)

Praise be to the LORD from Zion, to him who dwells in Jerusalem. Praise the LORD. (Ps 135:21)

The LORD builds up Jerusalem. Extol the LORD, O Jerusalem; praise your God, O Zion, for he strengthens the bars of your gates and blesses your people within you. He grants peace to your borders and satisfies you with the finest of wheat. (Ps 147:2, 12–14)

The LORD will surely comfort Zion and will look with compassion on all her ruins; he will make her deserts like Eden, her wastelands like the garden of the LORD. Joy and gladness will be found in her, thanksgiving and the sound of singing. (Is 51:3)

Thank you, LORD, we are glad and rejoice forever in what you will create, for you will create Jerusalem to be a delight and its people a joy. (Is 65:18)

LORD, we long to see that you, the LORD our God, dwell in Zion, your holy hill. We pray Jerusalem will be holy; never again will foreigners invade her. (Jl 3:17)

LORD, prepare your people for on that day living water will flow out from Jerusalem. (Zec 14:8)

You promised, Oh LORD, that you would be a ring of fire around (Jerusalem) and you will be its glory within. (Zec 2:5)

Prepare us to see the Holy City, the new Jerusalem, coming down out of heaven from you, God, prepared as a bride beautifully dressed for her husband. (Rv 21:2)

WEDNESDAY

Ascribe to the LORD the glory due his name. Bring an offering and come before him; worship the LORD in the splendor of his holiness.
1 Chronicles 16:29

Wednesday

Date _____

Waiting on the LORD

_____

_____

_____

Worship

_____

_____

_____

Wounded and Sick

_____

_____

_____

Peace in Jerusalem

_____

_____

_____

WEDNESDAY

At his tabernacle I will sing and make music to the LORD.
Psalm 27:6b

Wednesday

Date _____

Waiting on the LORD

_____

_____

_____

Worship

_____

_____

_____

Wounded and Sick

_____

_____

_____

Peace in Jerusalem

_____

_____

_____

WEDNESDAY

I will heal my people and let them enjoy abundant peace and security. I will bring Israel back from captivity and rebuild them as they were before.
Jeremiah 33:6b–7

Wednesday

Date _____

Waiting on the LORD

_____

_____

_____

Worship

_____

_____

_____

Wounded and Sick

_____

_____

_____

Peace in Jerusalem

_____

_____

_____

WEDNESDAY

Your love is ever before me, and I walk continually in your truth.
Psalm 26:3

Wednesday

Date _____

Waiting on the LORD

_____

_____

_____

Worship

_____

_____

_____

Wounded and Sick

_____

_____

_____

Peace in Jerusalem

_____

_____

_____

WEDNESDAY

Sing to the LORD a new song, for he has done marvelous things;
his right hand and his holy arm have worked salvation for him.
Psalm 98:1

Wednesday

Date _____

Waiting on the LORD

_____
_____
_____

Worship

_____
_____
_____

WEDNESDAY

Wounded and Sick

_____
_____
_____

Peace in Jerusalem

_____
_____
_____

*By day the LORD directs his love, at night his song is with me
a prayer to the God of my life.*
Psalm 42:8

Wednesday

Date _____

Waiting on the LORD

_____

_____

_____

Worship

_____

_____

_____

Wounded and Sick

_____

_____

_____

Peace in Jerusalem

_____

_____

_____

WEDNESDAY

I have posted watchmen on your walls, O Jerusalem; they will never be silent day or night. You who call on the LORD, give yourselves no rest, and give him no rest till he establishes Jerusalem and makes her the praise of the earth.
Isaiah 62:6–7

Wednesday

Date ——————

Waiting on the LORD

———————————————————————————
———————————————————————————
———————————————————————————

Worship

———————————————————————————
———————————————————————————
———————————————————————————

Wounded and Sick

———————————————————————————
———————————————————————————
———————————————————————————

Peace in Jerusalem

———————————————————————————
———————————————————————————
———————————————————————————

WEDNESDAY

Come, let us bow down in worship, let us kneel before the LORD our Maker.
Psalm 95:6

Wednesday

Date _____

Waiting on the LORD

_____

_____

_____

Worship

_____

_____

_____

Wounded and Sick

_____

_____

_____

Peace in Jerusalem

_____

_____

_____

WEDNESDAY

He has made everything beautiful in its time. He has also set eternity in the hearts of men; yet they cannot fathom what God has done from beginning to end.
Ecclesiastes 3:11

Wednesday

Date ⸻

Waiting on the LORD

⸻

⸻

⸻

Worship

⸻

⸻

⸻

Wounded and Sick

⸻

⸻

⸻

Peace in Jerusalem

⸻

⸻

⸻

WEDNESDAY

There is a time for everything, and a season for every activity under heaven: a
time to weep and a time to laugh, a time to mourn and a time to dance.
Ecclesiastes 3:1, 4

Wednesday

Date _____

Waiting on the LORD

_____

_____

_____

Worship

_____

_____

_____

Wounded and Sick

_____

_____

_____

Peace in Jerusalem

_____

_____

_____

WEDNESDAY

*In him we have redemption through his blood, the forgiveness of sins,
in accordance with the riches of God's grace.*
Ephesians 1:7

Wednesday

Date _____

Waiting on the LORD

_____

_____

_____

Worship

_____

_____

_____

Wounded and Sick

_____

_____

_____

Peace in Jerusalem

_____

_____

_____

WEDNESDAY

Thursday

Intercessory Prayer Guide

Thanksgiving

Thank God for your blessings of at least one item in each category.

Material Blessings: house, car, clothes, shoes, food, computers

Physical Blessings: health, eyes, mouth, mind, hands, toes

Spiritual Blessings: faith, spiritual gifts, forgiveness, prayer, grace, music, fruit of the Spirit (Gal 5:22–23)

Eternal Blessings: people—family, friends, church body, treasures

Let us come before him with thanksgiving and extol him with music and song. (Ps 95:2)

Give thanks to the LORD, for he is good. *His love endures forever.* Give thanks to the God of gods. *His love endures forever* . . . To him who alone does great wonders, *his love endures forever.* Who by his understanding made the heavens, *his love endures forever* . . . To the One who remembered us in our low estate. *His love endures forever.* Give thanks to the God of heaven. *His love endures forever.* (Ps 136:1–9, 23–26)

I will praise God's name in song and glorify him with thanksgiving. (Ps 69:30)

I always thank my God as I remember you in my prayers. (Phil 1:4)

I urge, then, first of all, that requests, prayers, intercession and thanksgiving be made for everyone— (1 Tm 2:1)

With thanksgiving, present your requests to God. (Phil 4:6b)

For everything God created is good, and nothing is to be rejected if it is received with thanksgiving. (1 Tm 4:4)

Thursday

Intercessory Prayer Guide

Extended Family

LORD, you have set before _____ life and death, blessings and curses. Now may he/she choose life, so that he/she and their children may live and love the LORD our God, listen to his voice, and hold fast to him. For the LORD is their life, and he will give many years. (Dt 30:19–20)

LORD, help _____ to do your will, O my God; may your law be within his heart. (Ps 40:8)

The LORD is near all who call on him, to all who call on him in truth. Be near _____ today. (Ps 145:18)

Give us unity and protect our family, LORD. We know a house divided against itself cannot stand. (Mk 3:25)

As we gather together, help us always be completely humble and gentle; be patient, bearing with one another in love. (Eph 4:2)

LORD, enable us to be responsible and provide for our relatives and especially for our immediate family when they are in need, so we do not deny the faith and become worse than an unbeliever. (1 Tm 5:8)

Let us pray for a son who dishonors his father, a daughter who rises up against her mother, a daughter-in-law against her mother-in-law—a man's enemies are the members of his own household. (Mi 7:6)

Help us to not gloat when our enemy falls; when he stumbles, do not let our hearts rejoice. (Prv 24:17)

If my enemy is hungry, help me give him food to eat; if he is thirsty, help me give him water to drink. (Prv 25:21)

Keep my tongue from evil and my lips from speaking lies. (Ps 34:13)

May the LORD direct your hearts into God's love and Christ's perseverance. (2 Thes 3:5)

Enemies, Persecutors, and EGR's—(extra grace required)

Thank you, LORD. You prepare a table before me in the presence of my enemies. You anoint my head with oil; my cup overflows. (Ps 23:5)

LORD, rid me of all bitterness, rage and anger, brawling and slander, along with every form of malice. (Eph 4:31)

LORD, we need your grace to slander no one, to be peaceable and considerate, and to show true humility toward all men. (Ti 3:2)

Wounds from a friend can be trusted, but an enemy multiplies kisses. (Prv 27:6)

I know that you are pleased with me, for my enemy does not triumph over me. (Ps 41:11)

Yet do not regard him as an enemy, but warn him as a brother. (2 Thes 3:15)

Thank you, you rescued me from my powerful enemy, from my foes, who were too strong for me. (Ps 18:17)

Deliver me from the hand of the enemy, ransom me from the clutches of the ruthless. (Jb 6:23)

Help me not to take revenge, but leave room for God's wrath, for it is written: "It is mine to avenge; I will repay," If my enemy is hungry, help me to feed him; if he is thirsty, help me give him something to drink. In doing this, I will heap burning coals on his head. I will touch their soul with kindness. (Rom 12:19–20) **THURSDAY**

Father, I need your grace to respond with a gentle answer which turns away wrath instead of a harsh word that stirs up anger. (Prv 15:1)

Help me not be like a fool who shows his annoyance at once, but a prudent man who overlooks an insult. (Prv 12:16)

You have heard that it was said, "Love your neighbor and hate your enemy." But I tell you: Love your enemies and pray for those who persecute you, that you may be sons of your Father in heaven. He causes his sun to rise on the evil and the good, and sends rain on the righteous and the unrighteous. (Mt 5:43–45)

For it is by grace you have been saved, through faith—and this not from yourselves, it is the gift of God—not by works, so that no one can boast.
Ephesians 2:8–9

Thursday

Date ─────────────

Thanksgiving

_____

_____

_____

Extended Family

_____

_____

_____

Enemies/Persecutors/ EGR's

_____

_____

_____

THURSDAY

For with the LORD is unfailing love and with him is full redemption.
Psalm 130:7

Thursday

Date _____

Thanksgiving

_____

_____

_____

Extended Family

_____

_____

_____

Enemies/ Persecutors/ EGR's

_____

_____

_____

THURSDAY

*Who, being in very nature God, did not consider equality with
God something to be grasped, but made himself nothing, taking
the very nature of a servant, being made in human likeness.
. . . He humbled himself and became obedient to death.*
Philippians 2:6–8

Thursday

Date _____

Thanksgiving

_____

_____

_____

Extended Family

_____

_____

_____

Enemies/Persecutors/ EGR's

_____

_____

_____

THURSDAY

Be on your guard; stand firm in the faith; be men of courage;
be strong. Do everything in love.
1 Corinthians 16:13–14

Thursday

Date _____

Thanksgiving

_____

_____

_____

Extended Family

_____

_____

_____

Enemies/ Persecutors/ EGR's

_____

_____

_____

THURSDAY

If I have faith that can move mountains, but have not love, I am nothing.
1 Corinthians 13:2b

Thursday

Date _____

Thanksgiving

_____

_____

_____

Extended Family

_____

_____

_____

Enemies/Persecutors/ EGR's

_____

_____

_____

THURSDAY

But the prayer of the upright pleases him.
Proverbs 15:8b

Thursday

Date _____

Thanksgiving

_____

_____

_____

Extended Family

_____

_____

_____

Enemies/ Persecutors/ EGR's

_____

_____

_____

THURSDAY

*Godliness with contentment is great gain. For we brought
nothing into this world, and we can take nothing out of it.*
1 Timothy 6:6–7

Thursday

Date _____

Thanksgiving

_____

_____

_____

Extended Family

_____

_____

_____

Enemies/Persecutors/ EGR's

_____

_____

_____

THURSDAY

I became a servant of this gospel by the gift of God's grace
given me through the working of his power.
Ephesians 3:7

Thursday

Date _____

Thanksgiving

_____

_____

_____

Extended Family

_____

_____

_____

Enemies/ Persecutors/ EGR's

_____

_____

_____

THURSDAY

Command those who are rich in this present world not to be arrogant not to put their hope in wealth, which is so uncertain, but to put their hope in God, who richly provides us with everything for our enjoyment.
1 Timothy 6:17

Thursday

Date _____

Thanksgiving

_____

_____

_____

Extended Family

_____

_____

_____

Enemies/Persecutors/ EGR's

THURSDAY

_____

_____

_____

Command them to do good, to be rich in good deeds, and to be generous and willing to share. In this way they will lay up treasures for themselves as a firm foundation for the coming age, so they may take hold of the life that is truly life.
1 Timothy 6:18–19

Thursday

Date _____

Thanksgiving

_____

_____

_____

Extended Family

_____

_____

_____

Enemies/ Persecutors/ EGR's

_____

_____

_____

THURSDAY

But to each one of us grace has been given as Christ apportioned it.
Ephesians 4:7

Thursday

Date _____

Thanksgiving

_____

_____

_____

Extended Family

_____

_____

_____

Enemies/ Persecutors/ EGR's

_____

_____

_____

THURSDAY

Friday

Intercessory Prayer Guide

Friends, Neighbors, and Coworkers

Help me, LORD, when I am weak not to covet my neighbor's spouse, or desire my neighbor's house or land, his possessions, or anything that belongs to my neighbor. (Dt 5:21)

Dear LORD, help me be a friend who loves at all times. Father, help me to obey your law concerning my neighbor, to love _____ as myself. (Prv 17:17, Mt 19:19b)

LORD, may I not forsake _____ and when disaster strikes give me humility to seek out help and receive it—better a neighbor nearby than a brother far away. (Prv 27:10)

Dear Father, you are the source of love. Give me your unconditional love for _____ as Jesus had and make me willing to lay down my rights, desires, life . . . Greater love has no one than this, that he lay down his life for his friends. (Jn 15:13)

God, help me serve with my whole heart in preaching the gospel of your Son. (Rom 1:9)

LORD, help me remain respectful to all people; to treat older men kindly and exhort them as if they were my own father, to treat younger men as brothers, older women as mothers, and younger women as sisters, with absolute purity. (1 Tm 5:1–2)

In my heart I set apart Christ as Lord. Help me always be prepared to give an answer to everyone who asks me to give the reason for the hope that I have with gentleness and respect. (1 Pt 3:15)

If anyone sees his brother commit a sin that does not lead to death, he should pray and God will give him life. (1 Jn 5:16)

FRIDAY

Friday

Intercessory Prayer Guide

Concerns and Ministries in Our Community, in America, and Around the World

But thanks be to God, who always leads _____ in triumphal procession in Christ and through him/her spreads everywhere the fragrance of the knowledge of him. For they are to God the aroma of Christ among those who are being saved and those who are perishing. To the one they are the smell of death; to the other, the fragrance of life. And who is equal to such a task? Unlike so many, they do not peddle the word of God for profit. On the contrary, in Christ may they speak before God with sincerity, like men sent from God. (2 Cor 2:14–17)

Make _____ aware that they themselves are your letter, written on our hearts, known and read by everybody. They show that they are a letter from Christ, the result of their ministry, written not with ink but with the Spirit of the living God, not on tablets of stone but on tablets of human hearts. (2 Cor 3:3)

The fruit of _____'s labor is from you, who reconciled us to himself through Christ and gave us the ministry of reconciliation. (2 Cor 5:18)

LORD, please equip _____ with everything good for doing your will, and may you work in _____ what is pleasing to you, through Jesus Christ, to whom be glory for ever and ever. Amen. (Heb 13:21)

Each one should use whatever gift he has received to serve others, faithfully administering God's grace in its various forms. If anyone speaks, he should do it as one speaking the very words of God. If anyone serves, he should do it with the strength God provides, so that in all things God may be praised through Jesus Christ. To him be the glory and power for ever. Amen. (1 Pt 4:10–11)

If _____ is insulted because of the name of Christ, they are blessed, for the Spirit and glory of God rests on them. (1 Pt 4:14)

I have planted you like a choice vine of sound and reliable stock.
Jeremiah 2:21

Friday

Date _____

Friends, Neighbors, and Coworkers

_____

_____

_____

Concerns and Ministries in My Community

_____

_____

_____

Concerns and Ministries in America and Around the World

_____

_____

_____

FRIDAY

But from everlasting to everlasting the LORD's love is with those who fear him, and his righteousness with their children's children.
Psalm 103:17

Friday

Date _____

Friends, Neighbors, and Coworkers

_____

_____

_____

Concerns and Ministries in My Community

_____

_____

_____

Concerns and Ministries in America and Around the World

_____

_____

_____

FRIDAY

*Then you will call upon me and come and pray to me, and
I will listen to you. You will seek me and find me when you
seek me with all your heart. I will be found by you.*
Jeremiah 29:12–14a

Friday

Date _____

Friends, Neighbors, and Coworkers

_____

_____

_____

Concerns and Ministries in My Community

_____

_____

_____

Concerns and Ministries in America and Around the World

_____

_____

_____

FRIDAY

I will satisfy the priests with abundance, and my people
will be filled with my bounty, declares the LORD.
Jeremiah 31:14

Friday

Date _____

Friends, Neighbors, and Coworkers

_____

_____

_____

Concerns and Ministries in My Community

_____

_____

_____

Concerns and Ministries in America and Around the World

_____

_____

_____

FRIDAY

I am giving you the service of the priesthood as a gift.
Numbers 18:7b

Friday

Date ⎯⎯⎯⎯⎯

Friends, Neighbors, and Coworkers

⎯⎯⎯⎯⎯⎯⎯⎯⎯⎯⎯⎯⎯⎯⎯⎯⎯⎯⎯⎯⎯⎯⎯⎯⎯⎯⎯⎯

⎯⎯⎯⎯⎯⎯⎯⎯⎯⎯⎯⎯⎯⎯⎯⎯⎯⎯⎯⎯⎯⎯⎯⎯⎯⎯⎯⎯

⎯⎯⎯⎯⎯⎯⎯⎯⎯⎯⎯⎯⎯⎯⎯⎯⎯⎯⎯⎯⎯⎯⎯⎯⎯⎯⎯⎯

Concerns and Ministries in My Community

⎯⎯⎯⎯⎯⎯⎯⎯⎯⎯⎯⎯⎯⎯⎯⎯⎯⎯⎯⎯⎯⎯⎯⎯⎯⎯⎯⎯

⎯⎯⎯⎯⎯⎯⎯⎯⎯⎯⎯⎯⎯⎯⎯⎯⎯⎯⎯⎯⎯⎯⎯⎯⎯⎯⎯⎯

⎯⎯⎯⎯⎯⎯⎯⎯⎯⎯⎯⎯⎯⎯⎯⎯⎯⎯⎯⎯⎯⎯⎯⎯⎯⎯⎯⎯

Concerns and Ministries in America and Around the World

⎯⎯⎯⎯⎯⎯⎯⎯⎯⎯⎯⎯⎯⎯⎯⎯⎯⎯⎯⎯⎯⎯⎯⎯⎯⎯⎯⎯

⎯⎯⎯⎯⎯⎯⎯⎯⎯⎯⎯⎯⎯⎯⎯⎯⎯⎯⎯⎯⎯⎯⎯⎯⎯⎯⎯⎯

⎯⎯⎯⎯⎯⎯⎯⎯⎯⎯⎯⎯⎯⎯⎯⎯⎯⎯⎯⎯⎯⎯⎯⎯⎯⎯⎯⎯

FRIDAY

Then Jesus said, "Did I not tell you that if you
believed you would see the glory of God?"
John 11:40

Friday

Date _____

Friends, Neighbors, and Coworkers

_____

_____

_____

Concerns and Ministries in My Community

_____

_____

_____

Concerns and Ministries in America and Around the World

_____

_____

_____

FRIDAY

*Hear my voice when I call, O LORD; be merciful to me and
answer me. My heart says of you, "Seek his face!" Your
face LORD, I will seek. The LORD will receive me.*
Psalm 27:7–8, 10b

Friday

Date _____

Friends, Neighbors, and Coworkers

_____
_____
_____

Concerns and Ministries in My Community

_____
_____
_____

Concerns and Ministries in America and Around the World

_____
_____
_____

FRIDAY

*You are the light of the world. A city on a hill cannot be
hidden. Neither do people light a lamp and put it under a bowl.
Instead they put it on its stand, and it gives light to everyone
in the house. In the same way, let your light shine . . .*
Matthew 5:14–16

Friday

Date _____

Friends, Neighbors, and Coworkers

_____

_____

_____

Concerns and Ministries in My Community

_____

_____

_____

Concerns and Ministries in America and Around the World

_____

_____

_____

FRIDAY

The Word became flesh and made his dwelling among us.
We have seen his glory, the glory of the One and Only,
who came from the Father, full of grace and truth.
John 1:14

Friday

Date _____

Friends, Neighbors, and Coworkers

_____

_____

_____

Concerns and Ministries in My Community

_____

_____

_____

Concerns and Ministries in America and Around the World

_____

_____

_____

FRIDAY

Grace to all who love our Lord Jesus Christ with an undying love.
Ephesians 6:24

Friday

Date _____

Friends, Neighbors, and Coworkers

_____

_____

_____

Concerns and Ministries in My Community

_____

_____

_____

Concerns and Ministries in America and Around the World

_____

_____

_____

FRIDAY

So do not be ashamed to testify about our Lord,. . . But join with me in suffering for the gospel, by the power of God, who has saved us and called us to a holy life—not because of anything we have done but because of his own purpose and grace. This grace was given us in Christ Jesus before the beginning of time.
2 Timothy 1:8–9

Friday

Date _____

Friends, Neighbors, and Coworkers

_____

_____

_____

Concerns and Ministries in My Community

_____

_____

_____

Concerns and Ministries in America and Around the World

_____

_____

_____

FRIDAY

Saturday

Intercessory Prayer Guide

Special Heartfelt Burdens

Even though I walk through the valley of the shadow of death, I will fear no evil, for you are with me. (Ps 23:4)

My guilt has overwhelmed me like a burden too heavy to bear. Praise be to the LORD, to God our Savior, who daily bears our burdens. (Ps 38:4, Ps 68:19)

My soul is weary with sorrow; strengthen me according to your word. (Ps 119:28)

LORD, you provide for those who grieve in Zion—to bestow on them a crown of beauty instead of ashes, the oil of gladness instead of mourning, and a garment of praise instead of a spirit of despair. (Is 61:3)

Be not afraid . . . for the open pastures are becoming green. For he has given you autumn rains in righteousness. He sends you abundant showers. He promises, "I will repay you for the years the locusts have eaten." (Jl 2:22a, 23b, 25a)

Jesus said, "Come to me, all you who are weary and burdened, and I will give you rest. Take my yoke upon you and learn from me, for I am gentle and humble in heart, and you will find rest for your souls. For my yoke is easy and my burden is light." I pray _____ will come to you and know that you are their rest when they are weary. Give them grace for the journey. (Mt 11:28–30)

Lord, the one you love is sick. (Jn 11:3)

Father, you tell us to carry each other's burdens, and in this way we will fulfill the law of Christ. Along with my prayers, show me how to help _____ carry their burden of _____. (Gal 6:2)

SATURDAY

Prayer for the Church and Pastors Locally, in America, and Around the World

(See Isaiah's Prayer for Jerusalem/Church in *The Invitation*)

Because I love _____, . . . I cannot remain silent. I will not stop praying for her until her righteousness shines like the dawn, and her salvation blazes like a burning torch. (Is 62:1 NLT)

I love the house where you live, Oh LORD, the place where your glory dwells (Ps 26:8). Therefore, as we have opportunity, let us do good to all people, especially to those who belong to the family of believers by praying for one another. (Gal 6:10)

Pray for his Glory. Not to us, not to us, but to his name be the glory! (Ps 115:1a). May (city, state) and the nations of the world see God's glory at our church.

So then, just as you received Christ Jesus as Lord, continue to live in him, rooted and built up in him, strengthened in the faith as you were taught, and overflowing with thankfulness. See to it that no one takes you captive through hollow and deceptive philosophy, which depends on human tradition and the basic principles of this world rather than on Christ. (Col 2:6–8)

Claim God's promises, pray for the fruit of his church and his kingdom to come. "My food," said Jesus, "is to do the will of him who sent me and to finish his work. Do you not say, 'Four months more and then the harvest?' I tell you, open your eyes and look at the fields! They are ripe for harvest. Even now the reaper draws his wages; even now he harvests the crop for eternal life, so that the sower and the reaper may be glad together." (Jn 4:34–36)

Go out through the gates! Prepare the highway for my people to return! Smooth out the road; pull out the boulders; raise a flag for all the nations to see. The LORD has sent this message to every land: "Tell the people of Israel, 'Look, your Savior is coming. See, he brings his reward with him as he comes.'" They will be called the "Holy People " and "the People Redeemed by the LORD ." And Jerusalem will be known as "the Desirable Place" and "the City No Longer Forsaken." (Is 62:10–12)

SATURDAY

Prepare Your Heart for Worship

Dear LORD, we consecrate ourselves in preparation for worship. (Num 11:18a)

He who sacrifices thank offerings honors me, and he prepares the way so that I may show him the salvation of God. (Ps 50:23)

Righteousness goes before him and prepares the way for his steps. (Ps 85:13)

A voice of one calling: "In the desert prepare the way for the LORD; make straight in the wilderness a highway for our God." (Is 40:3)

Be silent before the Sovereign LORD, for the day of the LORD is near. The LORD has prepared a sacrifice; he has consecrated those he has invited. (Zep 1:7)

LORD, it is written: "No eye has seen, no ear has heard, no mind has conceived what you, God have prepared for those who love you." (1 Cor 2:9)

If a man cleanses himself . . ., he will be an instrument for noble purposes, made holy, useful to the Master and prepared to do any good work. (2 Tm 2:21)

LORD, help us prepare our minds for action; to be self-controlled; set our hope fully on the grace to be given us when Jesus Christ is revealed. (1 Pt 1:13)

Now to you, LORD who is able to do immeasurably more than all we ask or imagine, according to your power that is at work within us, to you be glory in the church and in Christ Jesus throughout all generations, forever and ever! Amen. (Eph 3:20–21)

SATURDAY

I have sought your face with all my heart; be gracious
to me according to your promise.
Psalm 119:58

Saturday

Date _____

Special Heartfelt Burdens

_____

_____

_____

Churches and Pastors: Local, in America, and Around the World

_____

_____

_____

Prepare Your Heart for Worship

_____

_____

_____

SATURDAY

*And you will be called priests of the LORD, you
will be named ministers of our God.*
Isaiah 61:6a

Saturday

Date _____

Special Heartfelt Burdens

_____

_____

_____

Churches and Pastors: Local, in America, and Around the World

_____

_____

_____

Prepare Your Heart for Worship

_____

_____

_____

SATURDAY

The LORD will take delight in you.
Isaiah 62:4b

Saturday

Date ——————————

Special Heartfelt Burdens

———

———

———

Churches and Pastors: Local, in America, and Around the World

———

———

———

Prepare Your Heart for Worship

———

———

———

SATURDAY

*No eye has seen any God beside you, who acts on behalf
of those who wait for him. You come to the help of those
who gladly do right, who remember your ways.*
Isaiah 64:4b–5

Saturday

Date _____

Special Heartfelt Burdens

_____

_____

_____

Churches and Pastors: Local, in America, and Around the World

_____

_____

_____

Prepare Your Heart for Worship

_____

_____

_____

SATURDAY

For the grace of God that brings salvation has appeared to all men.
Titus 2:11

Saturday

Date _____

Special Heartfelt Burdens

_____

_____

_____

Churches and Pastors: Local, in America, and Around the World

_____

_____

_____

Prepare Your Heart for Worship

_____

_____

_____

SATURDAY

But the man who loves God is known by God.
1 Corinthians 8:3

Saturday

Date _____

Special Heartfelt Burdens

_____

_____

_____

Churches and Pastors: Local, in America, and Around the World

_____

_____

_____

Prepare Your Heart for Worship

_____

_____

_____

SATURDAY

But you are a chosen people, a royal priesthood, a holy nation, a people belonging to God, that you may declare the praises of him who called you out of darkness into his wonderful light.
1 Peter 2:9

Saturday

Date _____

Special Heartfelt Burdens

_____

_____

_____

Churches and Pastors: Local, in America, and Around the World

_____

_____

_____

Prepare Your Heart for Worship

_____

_____

_____

SATURDAY

But thanks be to God, who always leads us in triumphal procession in Christ and through us spreads everywhere the fragrance of the knowledge of him. For we are to God the aroma of Christ among those who are being saved and those who are perishing.
2 Corinthians 2:14–15

Saturday

Date _____

Special Heartfelt Burdens

_____

_____

_____

Churches and Pastors: Local, in America, and Around the World

_____

_____

_____

Prepare Your Heart for Worship

_____

_____

_____

SATURDAY

Therefore, brothers, since we have confidence to enter the Most
Holy Place by the blood of Jesus, by a new and living way opened
for us through the curtain, that is, his body, and since we have
a great priest over the house of God, let us draw near . . .
Hebrews 10:19–22a

Saturday

Date _____

Special Heartfelt Burdens

_____

_____

_____

Churches and Pastors: Local, in America, and Around the World

_____

_____

_____

Prepare Your Heart for Worship

_____

_____

_____

SATURDAY

Let us run with perseverance the race marked out for us. Let us
fix our eyes on Jesus, the author and perfecter of our faith, who
for the joy set before him endured the cross, . . . and sat down at the
right hand of the throne of God. Consider him . . .
so that you will not . . . lose heart.
Hebrews 12:1b–3

Saturday

Date _____

Special Heartfelt Burdens

_____

_____

_____

Churches and Pastors: Local, in America, and Around the World

_____

_____

_____

Prepare Your Heart for Worship

_____

_____

_____

SATURDAY

Surely I am with you always, to the very end of the age.
Matthew 28:20b

Saturday

Date _____

Special Heartfelt Burdens

_____

_____

_____

Churches and Pastors: Local, in America, and Around the World

_____

_____

_____

Prepare Your Heart for Worship

_____

_____

_____

SATURDAY

To order additional copies of this book call:
1-877-421-READ (7323)
or please visit our Web site at
www.winepressbooks.com

If you enjoyed this quality custom-published book,
drop by our Web site for more books and information.

www.winepressgroup.com
"Your partner in custom publishing."